W9-CGY-375

163

Mysteries of the Universe

Mysteries

OF THE

UNIVERSE

William R. Corliss

THOMAS Y. CROWELL COMPANY

ESTABLISHED 1834

New York

CONTENTS

v

I I

I

NO BEGINNING, NO END?

On starry nights who hasn't looked up and wondered where the stars end? And, if there is an end to them, what the mysterious partition is like, beyond which there is truly neither atom nor the faintest ray of light. Ever more powerful telescopes find no end to the star fields that seem to sweep toward infinity. Perhaps there is no beginning and no end to space; perhaps time, too, is boundless.

Such all-encompassing thoughts demand a free-wheeling branch of science. Cosmology is its name. This highly speculative discipline deals with beginnings and ends, the size of the universe, its rhythm and structure, and the laws that describe the motions of whole galaxies as well as the smallest atoms of interstellar gas. Of all the sciences, cosmology paints the biggest picture with the thinnest paint. Because its facts are few and "soft," cosmology is torn by warring schools of thought, each with voluble champions. This makes cosmology an exciting frontier of science.

To be more specific, today's cosmology tries to answer the following questions:

How big is the universe?
How old is it, and what has been its history?
How is matter distributed throughout space?

1

Are terrestrial physical laws applicable to the far galaxies?
Whence comes the energy to run the universe?
Are the different chemical elements present in the same propor-
tions throughout the universe?

Thinly concealed behind these questions are two of the oldest
queries of reflective man: where did we come from and where are
we going?

Missing from the list are all questions involving *why*. Cosmology,
like any true science, would be content merely with an accurate and
esthetically appealing description of the cosmos. The *why* tran-
scends pure science but not the mental ambition of man. The role
of science was expressed with precision by Newton:

"Natural philosophy consists in discovering the frame and opera-
tions of nature, and reducing them, as far as may be, to general
rules or laws—establishing these rules by observations and experiments, and thence deducing the causes and effects of things . . ."

The methods of cosmology differ from, say, mechanics. In mechanics one goes to the laboratory and measures the velocity of a
falling weight, or clocks the oscillations of a pendulum bob. One
searches for regularities in the data and from them evolves physical
theories. Furthermore, one can always go back to the lab and check
theory as often as desirable. The laboratory of cosmology is the
whole universe. Cause-and-effect experiments are circumscribed by
that proportionately tiny radius of action attainable by spacecraft.
For the most part, cosmologists must be content with messages
brought from the reaches of the universe by a few feeble radio
waves and rays of light. They can only surmise how these photonic
messages may have been distorted in the billions of years they took
to get here.

The challenge of cosmology has attracted some of the best scientific minds in the world. They play the "game" of cosmology in
this way:

The available data are lined up and judged according to the
ability of the man who measured them and the instruments he
employed. In cosmology, most facts come from radio and optical
telescopic observations, for cosmology is primarily an *observational* science. Supporting data include meteorite chemical analyses and radioactive dating of terrestrial materials.

Using intuition and artistry, the cosmologist next constructs a theoretical model of the universe that accounts for all salient facts. Cosmologists try to make their models simple, symmetric, uniform, and deserving of other adjectives associated with the scientist's concept of beauty. (How presumptuous of the cosmologists! The universe need not be beautiful.)

Finally, the model must be tested against new facts as they appear. Since there are normally as many models as there are cosmologists, experiments must be made to force a choice. If no models satisfy the facts, new ones must be created.

Cosmology is a game that never ends. As new instruments are built for probing the cosmos, new facts demolish the best theories and the above cycle is repeated.

Suppose you undertook personally the task of working out the nature of the universe—that is, constructing a cosmology from scratch. With your naked eyes, you could pick out a few thousand bright stars, six of the planets that wander across the background of the stars, and, of course, the sun and moon. You would even be able to see one of the nearest galaxies, the Great Nebula in Andromeda, 2,500,000 light-years * away, but it would appear only as another star. None of its rich detail, its billions of swirling stars, nor its tremendous distance could be discerned with the naked eye. You would be in the position of Ptolemy and the astronomers of ancient Greece and Egypt, who with great patience catalogued the erratic planets and the risings and settings of the sun and moon. With crude sighting devices, these men predicted eclipses and constructed calendars for agricultural and religious purposes. In short, they made crude mathematical models of the seeable universe above them. Sometimes physical models were built. Farther north, in England, prehistoric men arranged the stones at Stonehenge so that they simulated nature's clock and forecast astronomical events, such as Midsummer's Day. To provide answers to why things are as they are, the ancients often considered the stars and planets to be the manifestations and playthings of gods and goddesses. These models were cosmologies—limited, but satisfying, and accurate enough for their assigned purposes.

* A light-year is the distance that light travels in a year's time. It is used as a unit in expressing stellar distances and is equal to approximately six trillion miles.

How much farther could you travel toward modern cosmology without telescope and spectrograph? Quite a way, surprisingly. Here is a case in point. Tycho Brahe, a sixteenth-century Dane and the last great naked-eye astronomer, patiently amassed many volumes of very precise planetary sightings. In the hands of his assistant, Johann Kepler, these observations were summarized in three laws of planetary motion. Isaac Newton (1642–1727) carried the mathematical synthesis of Tycho's data a step further when he announced the universal law of gravitation. With one relatively simple law, complex planetary motion was accurately described; a most satisfying situation for the scientist, who supposes that nature is not only comprehensible to man but also simple at its innermost core. Newton's great generalization of experience leads to one of the cornerstones of modern cosmology.

Newton applied his new law to the thousands of stars he saw marching from east to west. The stars must, he reasoned, be distributed uniformly through space. Any other arrangement would not be stable for, according to the law of gravitation, local concentrations of stars would be quickly pulled together into single masses. The outermost stars in such clusters would be pulled inward by the gravitational forces of their inner neighbors, because there would be no outer neighbors to pull against collapsing forces. This kind of reasoning also leads the unwary to the conclusion that the universe must be infinite in extent. If it were not infinite and had an outer boundary, it would be just another large cluster of stars that should collapse toward its center. Here, finally, are thoughts as sweeping and general as modern cosmology:

The universe is infinite.

Matter is uniformly distributed throughout the universe. (This is now called the *cosmological principle*).

The law of gravitation can be applied anywhere in the universe, even though it really describes only our experience within the solar system. Until spacecraft travel to other star systems, we have no choice but to extrapolate "locally verified" laws.

No one knows whether any of these statements are really true. Still, based only on observations made with the naked eye, one can begin to think cosmos-sized thoughts. The thoughts, moreover, are intuitively satisfying. Who would want laws that are not universal?

Who would want untidy clumps of stars cluttering up the otherwise perfect (that is, uniform) heavens?

The cosmological principle can be broadened to include the time dimension as well as distance. Expressing this supposition in mundane terms: the universe flows along on a steady, smooth river of time, which has neither source nor eventual sea, nor maelstroms or niagaras in between. The proponents of the Steady-State Universe, a theory discussed in detail later, have proclaimed this to be the *perfect cosmological principle*. It is termed *perfect* because it includes the four known dimensions, because it is complete and therefore satisfying, and because it can be formulated without recourse to complicated astronomical instruments.

Turning from speculation to fact, an observational cornerstone was set in place in 1826, when the German astronomer Heinrich Olbers wondered why the night sky was so dark. This question is more profound than it seems on the surface. Certainly every natural philosopher from contemplative caveman on knew that the night sky was dark. It *was* dark; and that was that. Olbers looked deeper and reasoned this way: if the stars are infinite in number, and evenly distributed, one should see pinpoints of light covering the whole sky, until it is all as bright as the sun. In actuality, the sky is dark, and the disparity must be explained. This is Olbers' Paradox, and any cosmology we formulate must resolve it.

An instinctive response to Olbers' Paradox is that most of the stars in an infinite universe are too far away to brighten our sky much. True, the intensity of their light drops off as the square of their distance; but every time the distance of the stars within one's ken is doubled, the number of stars is multiplied fourfold. Attenuation by distance is exactly compensated by the increase in the number of stars. Surely, one argues next, most of the radiation from distant stars must be absorbed by dust and gas in the vast interstellar distances. This does not resolve the paradox either, even if true, because the dust would absorb the radiation and would soon be heated to temperatures where it would become incandescent and just as bright as the stars themselves. We are left, then, with a paradox born of the conflict between the simplest kind of observation and the surmise that the universe is infinite in time and space.

Adding the telescope to the naked eye expands the knowable

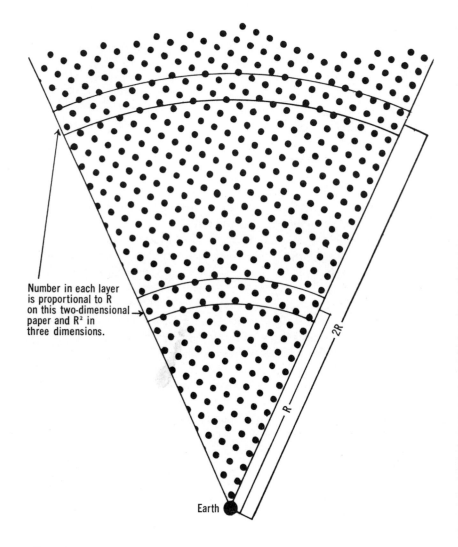

Number in each layer is proportional to R on this two-dimensional paper and R² in three dimensions.

Olbers' Paradox says that the night sky should be completely covered by bright stars in an infinite universe. The diagram shows how reduction in brightness with distance is just compensated by the increase in the number of light sources. Brightness *falls off* with the square of the distance and the number of sources *increases* with the square of the distance. Thus the total amount of light received from the stars along any given angle is the same, assuming the stars are distributed in an even manner throughout the universe.

universe many million-fold. Sample star counts tell us there are billions of stars in our own galaxy, and billions more in each of the billions of galaxies that stretch as far as we can see in all directions. (The total number of stars in the universe we can see has been estimated at 10^{21}.) Reflect, though. Does the telescope alone tell anything beyond sheer number, anything beyond the now-obvious fact that the universe is a big place? The answer is yes. Careful telescopic observation yields these two observations important to cosmology:

Matter seems fairly evenly distributed in the universe, supporting Newton's original hypothesis. Stars are organized into galaxies, and the galaxies themselves are clustered. (Our galaxy, the Milky Way, is one of a group of seventeen.) Despite this hierarchy, the cosmological principle is supported by the fact that all clusters and "clumpings" seem evenly distributed.

A distance scale based upon the relative intensities of stars and galaxies shows no bounds to the seeable universe.

A short digression on how to measure long distances is useful here. Distance and time (see Chapter 3) scales are so critical to cosmology that they cannot be ignored. The surveyor's device of triangulating for distance, even using the diameter of the earth's orbit as a base line (i.e., the parallax method), is good only out to about a thousand light-years. Beyond this distance, instruments cannot measure the tiny shifts in star positions (their parallaxes) as the earth moves around the sun. The method of parallaxes doesn't even take us beyond our own galaxy.

Consider another hypothesis. Given a street light one block away, we know that an identical street light two blocks away will appear four times fainter. A plan becomes clear; find stars of the same brightness, measure the distance of a nearby one by triangulation, and figure the distances of the rest by comparing their brightnesses with the known one. It's the street light method in reverse. In the closer galaxies, where telescopes can resolve individual stars, the famous Cepheid variables, first discovered in the constellation Cepheus, form the intergalactic rulers. The brightness of a Cepheid variable is a known function of the length of time it takes the pulsating star to go through its bright-dim-bright cycle. Astronomers pick out a Cepheid variable in another galaxy; they measure its period and apparent brightness; and knowing what its real brightness is from its period, they infer distance from the decrease in brightness. When Cepheid variables cannot be found, the brightest star of the blue giant type in the galaxy being measured is assumed to possess the same brightness as the brightest blue giant in our own galaxy.

In galaxies so distant that single stars cannot be resolved, the brightest galaxy in the local cluster of galaxies is assumed to be of the same brightness as the brightest in a closer group at a known distance. In a sense, this is a house of cards, with the foundation built from parallax measurements. The Cepheid variable distance scale rests on top of parallax measurements and so on. One wonders about the validity of this structure. Perhaps intergalactic dust absorbs some of the light from the reference stars; perhaps the brightest blue giant in Galaxy X is actually one hundred times brighter than its counterpart in Galaxy Y. Astronomers probably have bad dreams about this unsteady construction, but there are no real alternatives in an observational science.

Now, let us put this yardstick to work in cosmology. The story begins in 1912 when V. M. Slipher, an American astronomer, began a study of distant galaxies with a spectroscope. The expectation was that the spectrograph would disperse the light from the galaxies into a spectrum of lines similar to those emitted by the elements found in stars in our own galaxy. When the spectrograms were studied, however, the spectral lines were not quite where they were expected on the photographic plates. The H and K lines of ionized calcium, which are strong and easily identified, were shifted toward the red, that is, toward longer wave-lengths. Hundreds of galaxies show this shift of spectral lines toward the red, though none in our local system of seventeen do. The spectroscope thus introduced a new feature of the universe that every cosmological model must account for.

What would cause a red shift of galactic spectra? The first and most obvious explanation was the Doppler effect; that is, the outward motion of the galaxies relative to the earth "stretched" the light waves, lowering their frequencies. Most of the galaxies measured with the spectroscope would be moving away by this token because their spectra were "stretched" out; i.e., shifted toward the red end of the spectrum. Other interpretations of the red shift are possible. Possibly the light is shifted in transit by interaction with dust, like the redder light of the setting sun. Most astronomers and cosmologists now accept the red shift to be the result of the Doppler effect.

The red shift and intergalactic distance scale were welded together by the American astronomers Edwin P. Hubble and his associate Milton Humason, who, incidentally, began his career as a janitor at Mt. Wilson. In 1929 they showed that the velocities of the receding galaxies roughly doubled as their distances doubled. In other words, the ratio of recession velocity to distance, V/D, turned out to be roughly constant. Today's measurements of the *Hubble Constant* show it to be approximately:

$$\frac{V}{D} = \frac{1 \text{ kilometer per second}}{3 \times 10^{17} \text{ kilometers}} = \frac{1}{3 \times 10^{17} \text{ sec}}$$

The constancy of V/D was quite a surprise when it was finally confirmed by many observations. Almost all galaxies seem to be flying away from us, some at nearly half the speed of light; and, as we shall see, it is from this particular observation that sophisticated cosmologies are born. After all, it is not very satisfying to say only that the universe is big and uniform. We would like to know what it was like in the past, what gives it its present structure, and how it is evolving. The observation of a general motion within the universe implies a dynamic history—perhaps even a beginning and an end.

First, though, consider the reciprocal of the Hubble Constant. It has the dimension of time; it is equal to roughly ten billion years; and it seems to be the same for most galaxies measured. Could this be the age of the seeable universe? It can be interpreted as the time each galaxy would take to reach its presently measured distance from earth if it moved at its present velocity. But perhaps this view is naive. In the few decades we have been observing galaxies, we have taken only a snapshot of the universe during an almost infinitely small segment of its existence. To make things more confusing, this snapshot captures light from stars so distant that we see them as they were billions of years ago. Light's finite velocity gives us a time machine of sorts. For all we know, the distant galaxies may have already exploded or died peacefully of old age. Caution is advisable when we know so little.

Hubble actually did assume that the reciprocal of his constant was the age of the universe. At the time (1929), measurements of the Hubble Constant put the age of the universe at just under two billion years; a figure less than half that measured by geologists using radioactive dating. Different lines of evidence clashed head on, forcing astronomers and geologists to carefully reevaluate their positions. This productive conflict was resolved in 1942, when the German-born Walter Baade, taking advantage of the wartime blackout of Los Angeles, began a careful study of the Andromeda galaxy from the Mt. Wilson Observatory using its 100-inch telescope. Baade discovered that the Cepheid variables used by Hubble in his measurements of distance actually consisted of two distinct populations with different brightness-period laws. Hubble had treated both types of Cepheids identically in his work. Baade's correction in effect made the universe much bigger and pushed its age up to the five billion years desired by the geologists of his day. Like all preceding estimates of the size and age of the universe, Baade's corrections fell far short of today's estimates; viz., ten to fifteen billion years, based upon radioactive decay and other natural "clocks." (See Chapter 3.)

The vision of the universe given to us by Hubble has been popularly termed the "expanding universe." The common analogy likens the galaxies to spots on the surface of a balloon that is being inflated. As the rubber stretches, all the spots move away from one another. The physical picture can be made more realistic by imagining a whole series of dot-covered balloons, one within the other, and all being blown up simultaneously in a way that increases the spacing between balloons. If one made his home on one of these dots, no matter which one, he would see all other dots moving away from him. Is this physical picture a correct interpretation of the evidence? Is there an outermost balloon?

Imagine a moving picture taken of the "expanding universe" in which each minute of running time is equal to a billion years. Running the movie ahead into the future, would we see the galaxies receding farther and farther and ultimately moving out of sight as they attain the speed of light? George Gamow, the Russian-American cosmologist, and other proponents of Georges Lemaitre's Big-Bang Theory or "evolutionary cosmology" say *yes!* Adherents of the Steady-State Theory marshaled by the astronomer Fred Hoyle counter with *no!* So—the battle is joined. The Big-Bang Theory is more in vogue today, so we'll consider it first.

The Big-Bang Theory is a model of the cosmos, an analytical model that permits us to travel back and forth in time via mathematics. If we could actually build it, like a model airplane or some very clever planetarium, it would show us the evolution of the

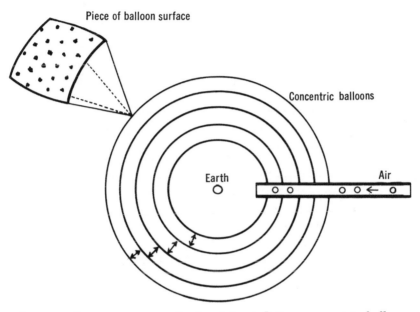

The expanding universe as simulated by inflating, concentric balloons. As each balloon inflates, surface dots representing galaxies move away from each other as the rubber stretches. For a three-dimensional analogy, the spacing between adjacent balloons must also increase with time.

universe from the moment of creation (a colossal cataclysm in this model) through the present, and as far beyond as we wished to watch the show. The Big-Bang Theory (and any other model) should achieve the following goals:

Resolve Olbers' Paradox.
Account for Hubble's Constant; i.e., the red shift.
Be consistent with the cosmological principle.

Not be at variance with the independently measured age of the earth.

Not violate any of the keystone physical laws derived from terrestrial experiments.

Be esthetically satisfying.

Having set the stage with the essential props, flick the switch on the movie projector into reverse and observe all the galaxies converging upon the earth instead of flying away. In the Big-Bang Theory, they will all coalesce into an immense glob of primordial matter and/or energy called *ylem* by George Gamow. (He borrows the term from Aristotle, who applied it to the basic substance of the universe.) This is the start of the film, representing the beginning of time in this cosmology. Any footage taken before this moment would presumably show God, or some first principle at work or (and we cannot eliminate the possibility) a contraction of some previous universe into the ylem. Such a cyclic, ever-repeating universe suggests itself; but, there exists no *known* force that can pull the fleeing galaxies we see today back into a ylem. All galaxies have passed the escape velocity and cannot be recaptured by gravitation although some as yet unknown force might cause contraction. Either we are seeing the final breath of the cyclic universe (an exhalation) or the postulated yelm materialized spontaneously from the void.

The Big-Bang Theory of the universe has been widely popularized, and today many are well adjusted to the idea that the receding galaxies might have been compressed originally into a sort of "cosmic egg." In the halcyon days before atomic bombs, *the thought of galaxies as debris from a stupendous explosion* did not appeal to many scholars. When the Belgian priest Georges E. Lemaitre introduced the idea in the late twenties it went unnoticed. Only when Sir Arthur Eddington recognized and promulgated the Big-Bang did it gain wide acceptance. Eddington later popularized the notion in his book *The Expanding Universe*, published in 1933. The Big-Bang idea is easily grasped by everyone, probably because we are all familiar with the result of earthly explosions. Popularizers of science like Eddington and Gamow (*The Creation of the Universe*) have been so persuasive that the Big-Bang's major rival, the Steady-State Theory, has been hard put to keep in the public eye.

Granted that the Big-Bang concept is easy to grasp, does it also explain the observed facts? It certainly explains the red shift because it was invented to do just that. The Big-Bang is not at variance with the cosmological principle because all debris from the explosion is uniformly distributed in space and expands in a regular fashion. Theoretically, expansions and contractions of the universe are the only large-scale motions permitted by the cosmological principle—overall rotation of the universe is prohibited, for example, because rotation implies a specific axis and an axis implies symmetry which precludes uniformity. Neither are any key laws derived from terrestrial experiments violated, for, as we shall see, the Big-Bang Theory relies heavily upon the results of terrestrial experiments, particularly those of nuclear physics.

Olbers' Paradox is resolved by an expanding universe. In the expanding universe, the velocity of light is reached at about ten billion light years. Galaxies, if they exist beyond this imagined spherical surface, cannot be seen by us because the light they emit will never reach us. Photons emitted in our direction by stars receding faster than light (assuming this is possible for the moment) would possess a net relative velocity *away* from the earth, just as a stone thrown off the end of a speeding train seems to move forward to an observer by the tracks. Readers familiar with Einstein's Special Theory of Relativity will deny that a physical object can recede from us faster than the velocity of light. The Special Theory indeed assumes this restriction, but the General Theory of Relativity, which we may apply in cosmology, does not necessarily prohibit these speeds. A finite *seeable* universe would produce the dark night sky that worried Olbers. The night sky should, as a matter of fact, become darker as more and more galaxies pass across the surface of that ten-billion-light-year sphere and become unseeable. The night sky is also darker because the Doppler effect shifts the light of the farther galaxies into the infrared, to which our eyes are insensitive.

The requirement for concurrence between cosmological and geological ages was mentioned earlier. Concurrence was not attained until Walter Baade revamped the cosmological distance scale with his discovery of two populations of Cepheid variables.

Now for the most subjective requirement, esthetic appeal. Is the Big-Bang Theory esthetically satisfying? The beginning seems rather messy, to be sure, for it is a discontinuity in space and time.

There was nothing and then there was something. There will be an end, too, for no known force can pull all the galaxies back together again. Some, however, prefer a beginning and an end rather than the hard-to-assimilate infinities of time and space inherent in the Steady-State Theory. It is really a matter of taste.

A bulwark of the Big-Bang Theory is its recounting of the birth of the universe—the story of a thirty-minute inferno that may have blazed ten billion years ago. Even the word inferno is a pallid metaphor for what George Gamow and his fellow Big-Bang enthusiasts propose for our genesis.

According to the ylem hypothesis, the universe was winked into existence as a huge centralized mass of elementary particles, mostly protons, electrons, and neutrons. The initial temperature of the ylem was billions of degrees, far hotter than the interior of the sun. The elementary particles were traveling at speeds close to that of light. This hot seething mass, from which all the stars and galaxies were to be born, must have been something like the core of a just-detonated hydrogen bomb, only incomparably bigger, denser, and hotter. The next chapter of the ylem story and many of its writers, too, are taken from the story of nuclear weapons development.

A nuclear fireball or mass of ylem must expand rapidly into its surroundings, and, as it expands, it will cool. The cooler the ylem gets, the more likely it becomes that the neutrons, protons, and electrons will stick together to form the nuclei of the chemical elements now found throughout the universe. If the known laws of nuclear physics show that cooling ylem would form stable chemical elements in the same ratios we find them today, the Big-Bang Theory will have strong support.

Examining the cooling process more closely, Gamow concludes that nuclear fusion of the elementary particles in the ylem must have created the elements we see today in about a half hour. Two facts indicate that the universe was flash-cooked rather than simmered for billions of years:

Free neutrons, which are needed to form stable nuclei, have a half life of only about twelve minutes. In thirty-six minutes (three half lives), only one-eighth of the original population would have been left, and further element building would have been difficult.

After a half hour, the ylem would have expanded and cooled to well below the temperatures needed for thermonuclear fusion.

The thirty-minute cooking would have caused protons and neutrons to fuse, creating heavy hydrogen deuterium. ($H^1 + H^1 \rightarrow D^2$) Similar fusion reactions would have given birth to tritium (H^3) and the helium isotopes (He^3 and He^4). At the end of thirty minutes, the universe would have been mostly hydrogen and helium, just about what we observe today. The heavy elements that make up less than one per cent of the mass of the universe would have been created by successive fusion of the heavy hydrogen and helium isotopes, providing a reasonable theoretical bridge can be built across the conceptual crevasse dug by nuclei of mass number five, which apparently cannot exist stably in nature. In other words, if we insist on counting by ones, we can never reach six because five does not exist. By fusing nuclei of masses four, three, and two in combinations greater than five, the Big-Bang Theory can bridge the crevasse and account for the observed abundance of the ratios of the elements. Gamow terms the present distribution of the elements, the "oldest archeological" evidence in existence. Of course, the synthesis of heavy elements still occurs to some extent in hot stellar interiors.

The energy for the Big-Bang, the biggest nuclear bomb ever assembled, came from the exothermic (evolutional heat) fusion of hydrogen nuclei. Propelled outward by the explosion, the primordial matter condensed here and there to form stars and galaxies, all of which still recede from the explosion point at high velocities. The galaxies we observe should thus be approximately of the same age. There is, however, a built-in time factor, for we see the distant galaxies by the light they emitted billions of years ago; some that have probably long since died.

Assuming the correctness of our astronomical distance scale, we should see the galaxies in various stages of evolution; the farther away they are, the younger they appear to us because of light's finite velocity. Now, galaxies do not necessarily age at the same rate. Some may rejuvenate themselves as new stars are formed from the condensation of dust (Chapter 5). If all old and dying stars were replaced by young stars, a galaxy would not appear to age at all. Astronomers identify two major types of galaxies: spiral galaxies, which seem to be self-rejuvenating; and elliptical galaxies, which do not. The latter would thus appear to be the best cosmological clocks because the aging process has not been affected by rejuvenation. Studies of distant elliptical galaxies show that they are much redder than the Doppler effect predicts. The conclusion is that the *excess* reddening is due to the fact that we actually see them as they were billions of years ago when they were younger, cooler, and therefore redder. Spiral, rejuvenating galaxies, on the

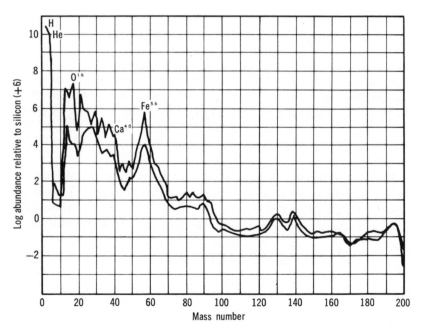

A good theory of cosmology should be able to predict how many atoms of each element survive in today's universe. After a thorough study of the seeable universe, cosmologists have plotted this graph showing the abundances of nuclei having the same mass numbers (same total of neutrons and protons). Upper curve applies to even mass numbers; lower curve to odd mass numbers. The Big-Bang Theory predicts the general shape of the curves, although it runs into trouble at the deep crevasse beginning at mass number 5.

other hand, show no excess reddening. The observation of excess reddening strongly supports the Big-Bang Theory, which supposes that all the galaxies were created at the same time. If new galaxies were being formed all the time, as suggested by the Steady-State Theory, the distant elliptical galaxies (our clocks) would be at different stages of evolution and indicate their different ages to us through different amounts of excess reddening.*

So much for the Big-Bang Theory. It is supported by many observations and meets the six conditions originally set up. The major problem is a certain lack of esthetic appeal; that is, the violence of a cataclysmic beginning and the slow, lingering death in the ultimate dispersion of all galaxies. But the beauty of a theory is a subjective thing; others might prefer to hear a starting gun fired and know that the race will eventually end.

Cosmology involves a conflict of personalities as well as theories. Nor are all the debates muffled by ivy-covered walls and the covers of scholarly journals. The two major theories of cosmology have champions noted for their verbal proficiency and inclination to carry their cases to the general public. On one hand, George Gamow backing the Big-Bang; on the other, Fred Hoyle, an English astronomer, who favors continuous creation and the Steady-State Theory. Neither theory has as yet overwhelming confirmation from observations of the cosmos, so there is ample room for persuasion and scientific politicking. Both theories meet the six basic requirements stipulated earlier.

The Big-Bang Theory had little competition from the time Lemaitre proposed it until 1948, when a group of scientists at Cambridge University laid the foundations of the Steady-State Theory. The chief architects were Herman Bondi and Thomas Gold, two Austrian-born cosmologists, and Fred Hoyle, its most articulate proponent today. Opposition to the Steady-State Theory, and the very thought of matter being continuously created, has been strong from the start. D. W. Sciama, who favors the Steady-State Model, says of it in *International Science and Technology:* "I think it is fair to say that most scientists reject it, but that an important minority consider the possibility of a steady state for the universe so attrac-

---

* An alternative interpretation of excess reddening blames intergalactic dust —an assumption that would require that 99% of the mass of the universe is dust.

tive philosophically that they prefer to keep an open mind until a decisive observation is made." This is a beautifully succinct statement of the present situation; also a clue to the philosophical lure of the Steady-State Theory.

The two main features of the Steady-State Theory follow directly from the *perfect cosmological principle* enunciated by Bondi, Gold, and Hoyle: viz., the properties of the universe are constant in *both* space and time. The consequences are:

The density of the universe is constant in time despite the receding galaxies suggested by the red shift. The Steady-State Theory postulates that matter is spontaneously created to replace that which expands outward. Using a cubic meter as a reference volume, the expansion of the universe, averaged over all of space, removes only two hydrogen atoms from this volume each billion years. These two atoms are replaced by the spontaneous creation of something from nothing. In more homely terms, this amounts to increasing the mass of the earth by one-seventh of an ounce in five billion years.

If the density of the universe is constant over all of time, creation and death of the universe are denied. There is no miraculous beginning and no infinite dispersion of matter at the end.

Reviving the earlier motion picture analogy, the film is now infinitely long. No matter when we choose to turn the projector on, we see the same average view of the universe. Details may change, but the major features go on forever. As the galaxies recede from the camera, they are replaced by new galaxies that coalesce from the ever-forming thin soup of hydrogen atoms. The pitcher never empties.

Who can deny the continuity, symmetry, and even beauty of the Steady-State universe? Well, some do. We live in a world of finite things: the distance driven to work and the number of days left until Christmas. For many, the jump from earthly finiteness to multidimensional infiniteness is something reserved only for God.

The philosophical attractiveness of the Steady-State Theory goes beyond eliminating the postulated centralized pot for "cooking" elements and, for that matter, dispenses with the services of the cook, too. Instead of saying in a cause-and-effect way that the universe we now see through the telescope is a result of singular, only-guessed-at events now long past, the Steady-State Theory clears the decks for this grand generalization: The universe exists and behaves only in those ways that perpetuate it; otherwise, it would have ceased to exist long ago. All physical laws, then, must be of such a nature that they preclude the scattering of galaxies and ultimate dispersion and demise of the universe; i.e., they must guarantee infinite stability if the Steady-State universe is to exist. Furthermore, the laws of the universe should be evident from present processes rather than through recourse to archeology because time is irrelevant in a universe with no historical events. Science and scientists love simple, all-embracing principles, and here they have one. Some biologists claim that life exists only to perpetuate itself; perhaps the universe results from a similar first principle.

The ultimate acceptance of the Steady-State Theory depends primarily upon observed facts. The Steady-State Theory fulfills esthetic requirements and also accounts for Olbers' Paradox and the red shift, roughly in the same way the Big-Bang Theory does. The expansion of the universe is not denied. Indeed, it may be the creation of new matter that forces it to expand rather than vice versa. The Steady-State Theory conforms to the cosmological principle and even surpasses it through the inclusion of time. The Steady-State universe cannot be at variance with the measured age of the earth, because we expect to find both younger and older stars intermingled. Through the telescope, we should see dying galaxies and those being born—and apparently this is the case. Overall age of a Steady-State universe is a meaningless concept.

The only consideration left insists upon the uniform application of terrestrial physics to the cosmos. Does the creation of new matter violate terrestrial laws? One answer says that the law of conservation of matter and energy applies only to finite volumes; and, since every hydrogen atom created in a cubic meter is balanced by one leaving, no conservation law is violated. The law of conservation of matter, which is merely a distillation of our terrestrial experience, can only be checked within limits. The rate of mass creation required by Bondi, Gold, and Hoyle is well below our most sensitive instruments and so does not conflict with actual experience. The Steady-State Theory also denies any increase in entropy (i.e., "order") for the universe as a whole because it demands an unchanging universe. Although physical processes here on earth exhibit seemingly inevitable increases in entropy, we cannot tell via the telescope whether the universe as a whole is running down.

In sum, the Steady-State Theory has much to recommend it to some scientists and philosophers, though it runs counter to many deep-seated instincts. So far, our observations of nature cannot exclude it as a possibility.

The essence and power of modern science lie in experimental verification or refutation of hypotheses. Only when two hypotheses cannot be resolved experimentally are scientists permitted the luxury of esthetic choice. This is the scientific method, the epitome of objectivity—except when it is twisted by a concern for tradition (viz., the initial resistance to the "unnatural" quantum theory) and by good salesmen. In cosmology, the experimental results are not yet conclusive.

Both the Big-Bang and Steady-State theories meet the six conditions stipulated initially. In addition, the Big-Bang Theory is supported by the observation of excess reddening for the distant elliptical galaxies, as discussed earlier. While it is true that the ylem hypothesis associated with the Big-Bang Theory does provide a possible mechanism for the formation of the various chemical elements, it had to assume the creation of working material, i.e., protons, neutrons, and electrons. This supposition of an act of creation is no more disturbing than that by the Steady-State Theory that all chemical elements have always been with us. Some cosmologists, such as D. W. Sciama, consider the element-building hypothesis a negative aspect of the Big-Bang Theory because there are many small discrepancies, any one of which could sink the Theory.

In searching for more conclusive tests of the two major cosmologies, it quickly becomes apparent that most tests depend upon accurate observations of very distant galaxies. The earth's atmosphere and ionosphere distort and absorb light and radio waves. The three tests suggested below depend in great part upon getting astronomical instruments out of the earth's gaseous envelope to where seeing is better. To this end, satellites now carry spectroscopes, X-ray detectors, and radio telescopes in increasing numbers.

Here are three possible ways to test the two theories:

1. The first test consists of a more detailed study of how galaxies vary in shape, size, and spectrum with distance. If there are

any systematic changes apart from the red shift due to the Doppler effect, the Steady-State Theory, which demands uniformity when galaxies are averaged over large volumes, will be disproved. The observed excess reddening of elliptical galaxies falls in this category, but many scientists consider the evidence inconclusive so far. A big telescope on a space station or the airless moon, where no man-made light interferes with observation, would be a great help here.

2. The Steady-State Theory also requires that the Hubble Con-

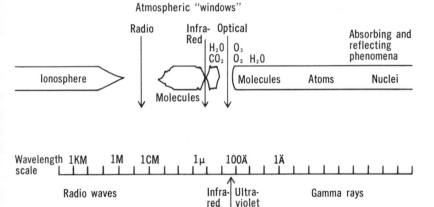

Absorption phenomena in the atmosphere permit only certain wavelengths of electromagnetic radiation to pass through to instruments on the ground. ($1\ \mu = 1$ micron $= 10^{-6}$m, $1\ \text{Å} = 1$ Ångstrom unit $= 10^{-10}$m)

stant remain constant as distance from the earth increases, i.e., expansion should be uniform. The data at hand are rather rough, but they do seem to indicate that the Hubble Constant increases with distance. A variant of the Steady-State Theory predicts that the velocity of galactic recession should decrease with time. The Hubble Constant for the more distant galaxies would thus be larger because we are seeing them as they were billions of years ago when they were receding faster. Again, more data are needed to settle the matter.

3. This test, like the other two, is aimed at the Steady-State Theory's obsession with uniformity, a relatively easy property to

test by passive observation from the earth. If the Steady-State Theory is correct, galaxies and any other astronomical objects should be sprinkled uniformly throughout space. We already know galaxies are, but how about other objects? The subject selected

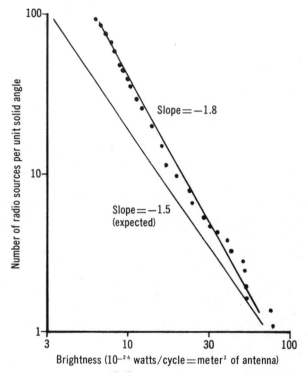

Counts of radio stars seen by big dish antennas seem to show that there are more of them than expected by the Steady-State Theory as distance increases.

for this census is the radio star, which has the advantage of emitting long wavelength radiation that is not significantly affected by the presence of interstellar dust. The test consists of measuring the intensity of each radio star and plotting the number of stars observed versus the various values of intensity. The number of radio stars seen within a sphere of radius R should be proportional to R^3, while the intensity of each observed star should be inversely proportional to R^2. If the radio stars are uniformly distributed and of the same average intensity, the plot of number versus brightness should result in a straight line with a slope of $-3/2$. The first counts of this type, made by P. F. Scott and M. Ryle, at Cambridge University, showed the slope to be closer to -1.8, a disappointment for the proponents of the Steady-State Theory. Still, the results must be rechecked; and, after the habit of science, the experiment will be duplicated by other observers.

Meanwhile, those who advocate the Big-Bang Theory are rather smug, because all data, preliminary though they may be, seem to refute the Steady-State Theory. The Steady-Staters are busy looking for modifications of their Theory that might save the essentials and yet account for the present tentative observations, should they be confirmed by other scientists and newer and better equipment. Even if the Steady-State Theory eventually falls by the wayside, it will have performed a noble feat, for it has made cosmologists sharpen their pencils and theories as well as improve their instruments. It is, after all is said and done, the *testable* hypothesis that is the most useful to science; it alone is specific enough to permit a yes or no on the ultimate battlefield of experimental truth.

Proving the Steady-State Theory wrong would not make the Big-Bang Theory right, though it would be the major contender left on the field. More tests would have to be formulated to prove it right or wrong. And if one cosmology dies, others will rise to take its place. Indeed, tomorrow's satellite- and moon-based instruments will certainly reveal new facets to the universe that will demand better and broader cosmologies.

———

READING LIST

BONDI, H. *Cosmology*, Cambridge University, 1960.
COLEMAN, J. A. *Modern Theories of the Universe*, Signet P-2270, 1963.
EDDINGTON, A. S. *The Expanding Universe*, Cambridge University Press, New York, 1933.

24 NO BEGINNING, NO END?

GAMOW, G. *The Creation of the Universe,* The Viking Press, New York, 1961.

GLASSTONE, S. *Sourcebook on the Space Sciences,* D. Van Nostrand Company, Princeton, 1965.

HOYLE, F. *Galaxies, Nuclei, and Quasars,* Harper & Row, New York, 1965.

――――. *Frontiers of Astronomy,* Harper & Bros., New York, 1955.

――――. *The Nature of the Universe,* Signet P-2331, 1960.

MC VITTIE, G. C. *General Relativity and Cosmology,* University of Illinois Press, Urbana, 1965.

MUNITZ, M. K. *Theories of the Universe,* Free Press, New York, 1957.

NORTH, J. D. *The Measure of the Universe: A History of Modern Cosmology,* Oxford University Press, New York, 1965.

SCIAMA, D. W. Modern Cosmology, *International Science and Technology,* p. 38, Feb. 1965.

SHAPLEY, H., ed. *Source Book in Astronomy, 1900–1950,* Harvard University Press, Cambridge, 1960.

SINGH, J. *Great Ideas and Theories of Modern Cosmology,* Dover Publications, New York, 1961.

2

QUASARS—
AT THE BRINK OF INFINITY

Every once in a while, Dame Nature comes up behind the scientists and kicks the complacency out of them. The discovery of radioactivity, the catching of the "extinct" coelacanth, and the finding of "organized elements" in meteorites have smashed many cherished fixtures in the temple of science. Eventually such unexpected, hard-to-digest events lead to new and stronger foundations for science; but until the new stones are in place intellectual anarchy seems to reign. Ever since quasars burst upon the astronomical scene in the early 1960s, astronomers and cosmologists have been wandering around with quizzical expressions. Nobody knows what quasars are; but whatever they are, no science-fiction writer has ever emplaced more energetic, more mysterious objects in the heavens.

Quasar = Quasi-Stellar Object: this reasonable condensation was suggested by Hong-Yee Chiu, a physicist at NASA's Goddard Space Flight Center. The word *quasar* is appealing to popular writers but apparently held in disdain by the astronomical fraternity. Semantics aside, everyone acknowledges that there are hundreds of perplexing "things" out there among the galaxies that we can see with radio and optical telescopes. Everyone agrees upon the salient features of quasars:

Some but not all quasars are strong radio sources—the fact that led to their discovery.

All quasars seem to be powerful emitters of visible radiation and all show a strong excess of ultraviolet light.

Quasars show large red shifts but no blue shifts.

The spectra of quasars are characteristic of a hot diffuse gas.

Quasars emit synchrotron radiation from accelerating electrons that are forced to move in orbits by a superimposed magnetic field.

Visually and through the radio telescope, many quasars show complex structures as well as pulsations in brightness.

Superficially, there seems to be nothing in this list to stir up a hullabaloo. The problem comes in trying to put the facts together in a consistent, reasonable model. (Of course, quasars may turn out to be unreasonable.) If, for example, the observed red shift is interpreted as a cosmological Doppler shift, the quasars are very far away and their brightnesses tell us that they must emit over one hundred times as much power as the biggest galaxies ever measured. If the red shift is due instead to gravitational pull on the photons leaving the quasar surface, quasars are close by, extremely compact and dense, and not likely to emit a spectrum typical of diffuse gases. The pieces just don't fit together.

Most astronomical speculators have busied themselves trying to figure out a mechanism capable of creating all the power implied by the first supposition—by far the current favorite. They haven't been too successful, but neither has anyone else who has tackled the quasar problem.

In short, astronomers have found a new species and cannot decide upon its pedigree. The next step is to take a closer look at the observed facts, construct models, and devise tests that will help us to decide between them, or, perhaps, build better models.

Astronomers have been looking at quasars for over a hundred years. Digging back through "sky patrol" photographic plates at Harvard, they have found quasar pictures taken as far back as 1888. But until the 1960s quasars were just other stars within our galaxy that emitted an unusual amount of ultraviolet light. They were "blue" stars consigned to the file of "miscellaneous oddities." They would be explained after the major features of the universe with its 10^{21} stars were established. Only when the radio telescopes with their huge dishes also picked up these blue stars did their eccentricities attract much attention. Here is a case where a new kind of instrument has helped astronomers pick important celestial objects from billions of companion stars.

Until very recently, we have known the heavens only through our eyes as augmented by the light-gathering power of telescopes. Our astronomical senses were extended into the radio region of the electromagnetic spectrum quite by accident. In 1931 an engineer, Karl Jansky, was working for Bell Telephone Laboratories in New Jersey, trying to discover the origin of the static heard on long-distance radio telephone links. After accounting for manmade radio noise and lightning flashes, he was still left with a weak noise source that he correlated with the passage of the stars overhead. Jansky even noted the concentration of radio noise in the constellation Sagittarius toward the center of our galaxy. This was the birth of radio astronomy. But Karl Jansky was more interested in communications engineering and he soon left this potential-packed offshoot of his work for others to follow up.

Jansky's discovery was well-publicized, but no one rushed to take up the challenge. Radio astronomy would have languished in the technical journals if it had not been for an enthusiastic radio ham named Grote Reber. Without federal grants and completely independent of organized science, Reber built a pointable thirty-one-foot-diameter dish antenna in his back yard. For a decade he was the only radio astronomer in the world. Reber discovered several radio stars and drew radio maps of those portions of the sky he saw from his Midwest home. Reber tried another technical experiment— the bouncing of radio signals off the moon. He failed; it was too much to ask of his home-built equipment. The publication of Reber's radio maps in 1942 revived interest in radio astronomy, but serious studies had to wait until the end of World War II.

Today radio astronomy is a respected adjunct of optical astronomy. With huge radio telescopes—the dish at Jodrell Bank in England is 250 feet in diameter—astronomers listen to (rather than "see") radio signals generated in the sun's corona, in Jupiter's radiation belts, in the atmospheres of radio stars, and of course in quasars.

To the radio astronomers the sky is not carpeted with untold billions of stars. There are no rings of Saturn, no spiral nebulae, no rich detail. Radio telescopes cannot resolve the filigree work. Furthermore, the radio sky is very dark indeed. Normal stars (except the sun) and galaxies do not emit enough radio energy for us to detect at all. Beyond the background "hum" at 1420 megacycles due to excited interstellar hydrogen, less than two thousand discrete radio sources have been pinpointed. Of these, only about one hundred have been correlated with objects we can actually see. In fact, radio maps and optical maps of the heavens have little in common. But in those few spots where congruence does exist, scientists have some tall explaining to do. More succinctly, radio telescopes locate problem areas that would otherwise be submerged in star fields that are too extensive even to count.

Initially, it was thought that all radio sources were within our own galaxy. Many are located near the galactic plane, but there is also a population spread evenly (isotropically) around the sky. This isotropic population must be either extragalactic and therefore independent of our galaxy's plane or so close to us and so weak that our sphere of detection lies within our galaxy's lens-shaped structure. Visual correlations support the first possibility.

What of the hundred or so radio sources that have been correlated with visible objects beyond the solar system? About half seem to be atypical galaxies, many with dumbbell shaped radio sources. Sometimes the radio and visible energy seem to be emitted by two or more distorted galaxies in near contact.* Some unusual, gas-rich spiral galaxies are also strong radio sources. Collectively, these are termed *radio galaxies*. Within our galaxy, gaseous nebulae and remnants of supernovae are powerful radio emitters. The other major source of radio energy consists of these "miscellaneous" blue stars called quasars.

On photographic plates, the quasars look perfectly starlike. Why aren't they just peculiar stars within our own galaxy? What makes them sensational and controversial?

For three years (1960–1963), the blue radio stars actually were

---

* In 1952, when Walter Baade first identified an important radio source in Cygnus as two colliding galaxies, there was a modest sensation. Now, colliding galaxies are passé—not enough kinetic energy involved and too infrequent to account for the many observations.

assumed to be members of our own galaxy. But no one could be positive whether they were inside or outside it without a way to measure their distances. In retrospect, the situation recalls the uncertainty over the location of the spiral galaxies early in this century. Were they far or near? Who could tell without that measuring stick? The ruler for spiral galaxies finally came along in the form of Cepheid-variables and red-shifts described in Chapter 1. Unfortunately, the spectral emission lines of quasars were few and could not be correlated with the lines of known elements. To make matters more difficult, quasars looked so much like nearby stars that large red shifts were not expected. Prejudgments were wrong; the unexpected was there.

On March 16, 1963, Maarten Schmidt broke the stalemate with a short paper in the British journal *Nature*. The title was: "3C 273: A Starlike Object with a Large Redshift." All the mystery of the quasar was inherent in that title. The 3C 273 indicates that the object in question was listed in the Third Cambridge (3C) catalog of radio stars. It was also a visible star with a large red shift. By December 1963 nine quasars had been located. The plot thickened as radio telescopes, optical telescopes, and spectroscopes all over the world were turned on these stars that were not stars.

Since the scientific world knew next to nothing about quasars, one might have expected an all-out program to pin down their characteristics with precision. This is not the way scientists work. There was no regimentation of men and equipment. Big instruments, such as the Jodrell Bank radio telescope and the 200-inch optical telescope at Mt. Wilson, are scheduled months in advance and are not diverted easily. Committees rather than individuals must make the decisions to look at quasars in these instances. If an individual scientist became interested in quasars, however, he could postpone his current studies and immediately swing his instrument around to the nearest quasar. Happily, the quasar is an intriguing enough object to turn the heads of the most conservative astronomers.

The experimental problem is this. The quasar photons and radio waves enter the earth's atmosphere and filter down to our telescopes and radio antennas. Can these signals bring us enough intelligence to divine the true nature of the quasar? With passive telescopic observation, we can hope to measure the following quasar attributes:

Quasar spectra—over wavelengths that can penetrate our atmosphere's radio and optical "windows." Actually, these windows are rather narrow. Spacecraft, if available, could measure radiation in the ultraviolet and X-ray regions of the spectrum.

Quasar angular diameter at both optical and radio frequencies. The two angular diameters may differ because radio waves and light waves have different physical origins.

Quasar shape; that is, whether they are circular, elliptical, or of more complex geometry.

Quasar visual and radio brightnesses as functions of time.

Polarization of quasar radiation. Many physical processes, such as accelerating streams of electrons, emit polarized radiation.

Number and angular distribution of quasars. Are they relatively common and uniformly distributed?

Absolute distance, diameter, velocity, and radiated power cannot be measured directly. They depend upon interpretation of the listed measurements. Most important of all is the distance scale assumed. For instance, if distance is known, angular diameter and brightness can be converted to absolute diameter and total radiated power.

Quasars are too far away to yield their distances to surveyor's triangulation (i.e., they show no parallax), even using the earth's orbit as a baseline. Neither do they seem to be associated with any galaxies at known distances. The only way to measure distance, then, is to measure any quasar red shift that may exist and assume it to be a cosmological red shift. This is precisely the breakthrough that Maarten Schmidt made in 1963.

Schmidt studied the optical spectrum of 3C 273, one of the brightest quasars. At first, no correlations of emission lines with those of known atoms could be made. Then, Schmidt noted three spectral emission lines that were related in a simple harmonic pattern (like piano chords), with separation and intensity decreasing toward the ultraviolet end of the spectrum. These three lines looked like the Balmer series of lines emitted by hydrogen-like atoms. The problem was that the lines were not where they were supposed to be in the spectrum. They corresponded to no elements known on earth. There was a key somewhere, and Schmidt found it; but to do so he had to ignore the rule that stars (remember that quasars look like stars within our own galaxy) do not show large red shifts. He assumed that the harmonically related lines were those of hydrogen and that they were shifted toward the red by 16%. The hydrogen Balmer H line, normally at 6563A, would then be at 7590A, in the infrared, and not even on Schmidt's spectrograms, as shown. The infrared H line was subsequently found by J. B. Oke of Caltech just where Schmidt predicted. In fact, once Schmidt broke the code, the spectra of other quasars became intelligible. They all

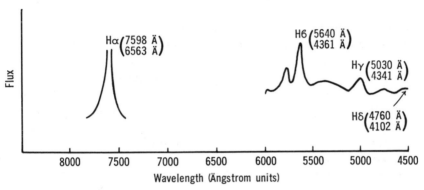

Spectrum of the quasar 3C 273 as measured by photocell. The hydrogen lines in the Balmer series would normally be found at the shorter wavelengths indicated in the parentheses. Instead they were discovered shifted toward the infrared by about 16%. The Hα line was shifted out of the visible and into the infrared. J. B. Oke found it just where Maarten Schmidt predicted it would be.

showed large red shifts. Lines of ionized magnesium, oxygen, and neon were quickly identified. The breakthrough in spectral analysis, of course, just deepened the mystery. Quasars were starlike with large red shifts and displayed spectra typical of hot, rarefied gases —a contradictory collection of facts.

So far, only the optical spectrum had been employed in the diagnosis of quasars. Fortunately, some also emit radio waves—otherwise who knows how long they would have been ignored by astronomy? The strength of the radio waves from 3C 273 has been measured as a function of frequency. The result (see below) shows that the radio flux drops off at higher frequencies. The shape of the curve resembles that recorded for synchrotron radiation; that is, radio waves emitted by electrons forced to move in an orbit by magnetic fields. Polarization measurements confirm the synchrotron theory. If the electrons were agitated by heat instead, the flux would drop off rapidly at low frequencies and be unpolarized. Radio astronomy thus gives us another clue to help unravel the quasar, at least that portion of it that transmits radio waves.

When we look at our sun, we see a bright disc adorned with dark spots, a corona, prominences, and other details the astronomers call "fine structure." On the other hand, a picture of the sun taken on a hypothetical film sensitive to radio wavelengths would show the corona extending millions of miles beyond the visible disc. It is not surprising, then, to find that the quasars look different at different wavelengths.

In the *visible* portion of the spectrum, quasars appear to be ordinary stars—superficially. Closer examination shows that some boast fuzzy halos. 3C 273, our favorite object of study, appears to have a spike or jet of material associated with it. The implication is that the quasar possesses an innocent, "normal star," facade behind which some untoward physical events take place.

Radio pictures of quasars confirm our suspicions. Many show dumbbell-shaped radio sources straddling the visible portion of the quasar. Many radio galaxies also show this kind of structure. This discovery is enough to arouse any astronomer's curiosity; but the problem is to see more detail with low-resolution radio telescopes. Fortunately, the moon occasionally passes in front of 3C 273, blotting it out for a few minutes. As the edge of the moon occults the quasar, a diffraction pattern is created by the moon's disc.* From the diffraction pattern, scientists can compute with precision the size and shape of the quasar's radio image.

In 1962 the moon occulted 3C 273 on April 15, August 5, and October 26. Three scientists—C. Hazard, M. B. Mackey, and A. J. Shimmins—working with the Australian 210-foot radio telescope, made diffraction measurements at 136, 410, and 1420 megacycles. Before the occultations, they had to saw several tons of metal from the telescope before it could be depressed to low enough angles. For hours before each event, all local radio stations appealed to

---

* A common diffraction experiment in college physics illuminates a penny with light from a pinhole. The shadow behind the penny shows light rings, and, at the shadow's center, there is a bright spot.

residents to turn off all transmitters during the few minutes critical
to the experiment. No cars were permitted near the telescope. To
underscore the importance of the experiment, duplicate records
were made and carried back to Sydney on separate planes.

The Australians' effort was not in vain, for 3C 273 was shown to
be a dumbbell radio source aligned with the visible jet. One of the
two elliptical ends of the dumbbell overlaid the visible starlike
image. Just what this all means is still a matter for conjecture. At

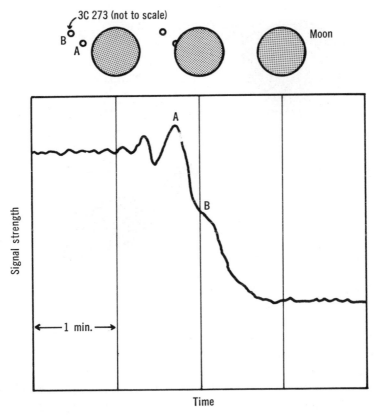

Radio diffraction pattern observed as the moon occulted 3C 273 on
August 5, 1962. Analysis of the pattern enabled scientists to measure the
sizes and spacing of components A and B with high accuracy. A similar
pattern was recorded as the quasar emerged from behind the moon.
(After Greenstein)

least, the astronomical theorists have new grist for their mills that
turn out quasar hypotheses and models.

The angular sizes of the visible and radio images of 3C 273 turned
out to be much smaller than normal galaxies located at the same
distance. Of course, the distance figure is based on the assumption
that the red shift measured for 3C 273 is due to the Doppler effect.
In short, *if the red shift indicates the quasar is far away, the quasar
seems much too small to generate the observed power level; if the*

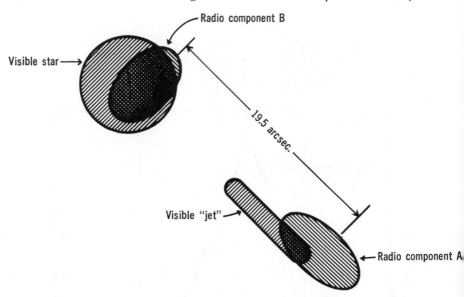

Radio and optical structure of the quasar 3C 273. The radio map was
made with the help of three lunar occultations.

*red shift is due to gravity and the quasar is close by, it must be
much more dense than any form of matter that we know.* Everything we discover about the quasar heightens the mystery.

To complicate matters further, a careful search through old star
plates revealed that some quasars exhibit cyclic changes in brightness. 3C 273 seems to show a thirteen-year cycle. In 1929 the
brightness of 3C 273 almost disappeared. In 1965 W. A. Dent published data indicating that quasar radio signals *also* fluctuate with
time. The short-term periodicity of quasars further supports the
contention that they could not be galaxies because galaxies are

thousands of light years across, and no overall changes in brightness could be propagated throughout a galaxy in thirteen years, even at the velocity of light.

It may be that the most extraordinary discoveries are yet to come. Perhaps with quasars, as with icebergs, we see only a small bit of the total picture. The several dozen quasars now identified were found only as radio telescopes singled them out from amid billions of similar star images. The astronomer Allan Sandage wondered whether some quasars might be too feeble in the radio portion of the spectrum to be detected. He therefore tried to find new quasars by checking all stars with excess blue light, a characteristic that quasars share with few other astronomical objects. He found a great many such objects—about two per square degree—which he calls "interlopers" or "quasi-stellar galaxies." Just how many of these interlopers, with the characteristic quasar visible spectrum but lacking its radio emissions, are really quasars is unknown. Some show quasar-like red shifts, and many interlopers are undoubtedly quasars. Perhaps we have been studying only that atypical variety that emits radio waves. It could be that quasars are abundant and represent a whole new facet of the universe seen by our telescopes but unrecognized all these centuries because they have masqueraded as ordinary stars.

Let us quickly review where we stand. The facts are these:

TYPE OF MEASUREMENT	QUASAR CHARACTERISTICS
Optical spectroscopy	Large red shifts. Spectra typical of hot, diffuse gases. Ultraviolet or "blue" excess.
Radio flux versus frequency with radio telescope	Radio spectrum similar to that from synchrotron radiation.
High resolution optical telescope	Starlike appearance, sometimes showing faint nebulosity or fine structure. Does *not* look like a galaxy. Rather small angular diameter.
High resolution radio telescope aided by lunar occultation	Many quasars show dumbbell-shaped radio sources associated with visible image. Some show even more complex shapes. Ra-

	dio image much larger than optical image.
Time studies with telescopes and old plates	Optical and radio brightnesses vary in cyclic fashion, with some periodicities as short as a few months.
Radio polarimetry	Radio waves are polarized as they should be for synchrotron radiation.
Counts with telescopes	The hundred or so quasars found with the help of radio telescopes seem evenly distributed. A great many radio-quiet objects (interlopers) possessing other quasar characteristics have been discovered.

So much for the facts. Now, what can be made of them? The above compilation gives us a quasar dossier that we can try to match with known astronomical objects. If the matching process fails, as it does, the dossier can be used to evaluate models that astronomers assemble with the help of physical laws and a good deal of imagination.

Before concentrating on the two major quasar models that have been proposed, it will be helpful to clear the field of miscellaneous theories.

We have already disposed of the old, once-popular, mechanistic, and intuitively satisfying galaxies-in-collision hypothesis. Visually, most quasars are single. Besides, colliding galaxies, though vastly more energetic than any true star, pale into insignificance beside the inferno that the quasar would have to be if it truly resides at galactic distances.

The quasar red shift might originate in the powerful gravitational force that an extremely massive or dense star exerts on photons leaving its surface. In effect, the force of gravitation pulls and stretches out the electromagnetic waves, lowers their frequencies, and shifts the whole spectrum toward the red. The so-called neutron stars do just this. The matter in neutron stars has been compressed so much that normal atomic structures have been squashed flat.

Neutrons and larger pieces of atomic debris called hyperons seem to be the stable form of matter in such stars. The density of a neutron star may be hundreds of thousands of times that of iron. It is even conceivable that some neutron stars are so massive that their gravitational force drags *all* photons back, preventing the emission of light, and making the star an unseeable object. Theorists have speculated that the biggest and "brightest" objects in the universe may not be visible to us. Could quasars be neutron stars that leak a little light? The answer is a fairly convincing *no*. The gravitational field at a neutron star's surface is far too powerful to permit the existence of the hot, diffuse gas indicated by quasar spectra. Most astronomers now concede that the quasar red shift is due to its high velocity away from earth.

Since quasars appear more starlike than galaxy-like, is it possible that they are members of our own galaxy that have been propelled outward at high velocities by some titanic explosion within the galaxy? Then the quasar red shift would *not* be a cosmological red shift and would not be related to distance through the Hubble Constant described in Chapter 1. So far, the idea seems valid; but considering quasar velocities (16% of the velocity of light for 3C 273 and over 80% for others), astronomers should have detected their headlong motions across the background of fixed stars long ago. The so-called proper motions of stars with much lower velocities are readily observable within our own galaxy. Quasars, then, are probably not high-speed members of our own galaxy, although they still might be fragments hurled out of the galaxy but which are now too far away to show significant proper motion but still not as far as neighboring galaxies. In astronomical parlance, quasars might still be "local" and extragalactic at the same time.

The quasar models that remain are not as refined as the Big-Bang and Steady-State cosmological models. Quasars are so new that theory lags behind experiment; although the theorists prefer to say that there are just not enough data to properly formulate a valid theory.

Fred Hoyle, the British cosmologist, and several other astronomers support the suggestion that quasars are high-speed debris from nearby galactic explosions. Support for this hypothesis comes from the fact that radio galaxies are known to explode with sufficient energy to hurl out masses equal to as many as ten million suns at velocities close to that of light. Conservation of momentum, of course, requires that one quasar projectile be balanced by another moving in the opposite direction. As a matter of fact, most radio galaxies show a dumbbell structure suggestive of action and reaction. Quasars, according to this model, are huge cannonballs shot out into space by radio galaxies serving as double-ended cannon barrels. The quasars associated with radio sources may be in the process of being fired out of the gun. Most quasars, however, should have traveled far beyond their guns; these would be the interlopers discovered by Allen Sandage. In 3C 273, we may be seeing the gun (a radio galaxy) with our radio telescopes and a single cannonball with our optical telescopes. The gun hypothesis is so new that its ramifications have not been explored. One of its major attractions is that quasars turn out to be reasonably sized objects with modest energy requirements instead of the monstrosities at the brink of infinity required by the next model. It is puzzling and not very reassuring that no quasars have been aimed at the earth—no quasars have been found with blue shifts. If the "local" model is correct we would expect to find some.

The final—and most popular—quasar model stems directly from the assumption that the quasar red shift is cosmological. The Hubble Constant then places many quasars at the very edge of the universe and, as mentioned earlier, the model must explain how such relatively small objects can generate on the order of 10^{39} watts of light power and 10^{37} watts of radio power.

Astronomers, like cosmologists, do not shrink from large numbers. Two energetic mechanisms have been suggested:

The most obvious source of energy is the nucleus. Possibly the quasars we see are chain reactions of supernovae, one explosion triggering another. Unfortunately, it is hard to see how so much power could be liberated by nuclear fusion reactions. The triggering scheme is not clear either.

Another source of energy is gravitation. If a mass equal to, say, one hundred million suns suddenly collapses in on itself, the power released could exceed that from nuclear sources by a factor of one hundred. The trouble here is that gravitational energy is released slowly at first and then rapidly at the final stage of collapse. It's hard to reconcile this schedule with observations. Rotation and fragmentation might be induced to slow the process. Actually, gravitational collapse might well be the energy source for the competing "cannonball" hypothesis.

Both of the above mechanisms run into troubles; and all troubles originate in the source of power which has its origin in the assumption of a cosmological red shift.

When all is said and done, the cement used to hold these models together is rather weak. Either the theorists are not imaginative enough in using the facts at hand or the facts are inadequate in quantity and precision.

When quasar models are constructed, it will be easy to say in retrospect that we now have enough facts to synthesize the correct model. Without such hindsight, the best course is to gather more data. We need to do much more asking. In particular, the spectra of quasars must be measured in other portions of the spectrum, especially in the infrared. The variability of quasar brightness in different portions of the spectrum is also a subject for concerted study. All spectra must be examined for Doppler shifts. If blue shifts are found, the model based on a cosmological red shift would be eliminated from the competition. On the other hand, if a careful search of the space around quasars reveals that quasars are actually members of galactic clusters—the discovery would confirm the view that they are among the most distant objects known rather than relatively near galactic projectiles.

READING LIST

BURBIDGE, G., and HOYLE, F. The Problem of the Quasi-Stellar Objects, *Scientific American*, 215, 40, Dec. 1966.

CHIU, H. Gravitational Collapse, *Physics Today*, 17, 21, May 1964.

GREENSTEIN, J. L. Quasi-Stellar Radio Sources, *Scientific American*, 209, 54, Dec. 1963.

HOYLE, F. *Galaxies, Nuclei, and Quasars*, Harper & Row, New York, 1965.

ROBINSON, I., et al, eds. *Quasi-Stellar Sources and Gravitational Collapse*, University of Chicago Press, Chicago, 1964.

TERRELL, J. Quasi-Stellar Objects: Possible Local Origin, *Science*, 154, 1281, Dec. 9, 1966.

3

MEASURING THE AGE
OF THE UNIVERSE

All entities of the universe—from galaxies to atoms—must interlock like a Chinese puzzle. The puzzle that is the universe has many dimensions. The dimension of time helps us to put the pieces together in the right sequence.

When we want to conquer distance, we jump in the car or take an airplane. Progress is marked by trees or clouds flashing by. Contrast these sensate things with intractable time. We are powerless to control its flow. No human sense directly detects the passage of time, although the day-night sequence and the seasons are natural clocks that give us imprecise impressions of passing time. Only when we contrive some device that translates time into the movement of clock hands or the action in an hourglass can we reliably and accurately perceive its passage. Of all the fundamental physical quantities—distance, mass, time, temperature, electric current—time is the most frustrating and elusive.

Yet we cannot allow ourselves to be discouraged about time because it is inextricably woven into the fabric of the universe we are trying to plumb. A good time scale is essential to understanding what has gone by and, by extrapolation, where we are going.

How do we measure time? With a clock, obviously. But in astronomy we wish to measure age, which is *accumulated* time. Conventional clocks tell us only of time's passage. They repeat themselves after twelve or twenty-four hours. Recorded history has accumulated a few thousand years for us, but this is hardly a grain of sand in cosmology's hourglass. Time computers reading in billions of years have to be found.

In the table following this paragraph some important time scales are categorized: first, according to the portion of history where they apply; and second, according to whether they involve simple counting (tree rings) or some cumulative effect (radioisotope disintegration). A key assumption inherent in all time scales that extrapolate us back to pre-earth and pre-sun times is that physical processes have remained unchanged. In radioisotope dating, for instance, we have to assume that the cosmic-ray flux incident on the earth has remained constant and has transmuted elements at a fixed rate. In measuring the red shift of distant galaxies, we analyze light that originated many billions of years ago. If the electrostatic forces holding electrons to nuclei were weaker then, our red-shift time scale would be faulty. It is therefore critical to our time keeping to build many clocks based on different physical processes. The better these interlocking and overlapping time scales agree, the more confidence we have in our age estimates.

A hierarchy in time aids clock building: man and his works are younger than the earth; the earth is younger than the solar system; the solar system is younger than the Milky Way; and the Milky Way is younger than the universe as a whole. These are assumptions, it is true, but pretty good ones. It is highly unlikely, for example, that the earth was born in an older star system and subsequently captured by the sun. Any time scale we devise or any *system* of interlocking time scales must confirm the above birth sequence.

Counting tree rings to measure the age of the sun is manifestly ridiculous, but tree rings are useful in archeology and help tie down recent events to a baseline. All of time's baselines consist of similar continuous, cumulative records of selected physical processes. These processes are used in calibrating time measurements in the otherwise inviolate past. To illustrate, scientists calculate the rate at which radioactive isotopes disintegrate from day to day with accurate conventional clocks. If there are 100 grams of isotope X in a sample at noon on Monday but only 50 grams left at noon on Friday, the half life of isotope X is four days. Isotopes with half lives

SOME KINDS OF "CLOCKS" USED IN DATING THE PAST

	RECORDED HISTORY (0–4000 YEARS)	EARTH HISTORY (0–4.5 BILLION YRS.)	SOLAR-SYSTEM HISTORY (0–5 BILLION YRS.)	HISTORY OF THE UNIVERSE (0–15 BILLION YRS.)
Counting Schemes	Calendars (earth's rotation and solar orbit) Tree rings Varves (sediment layers) Eclipses and other regular astronomical events	Climatic cycles (ice ages) Varves	None	None
Cumulative Physical Processes	Radioisotope decay	Radioisotope decay Geological processes: weathering and erosion, deposition, folding, tectonic movements Biological evolution Accumulation of salt in ocean Marine transgression Changes in earth's magnetic field	Stellar theory Radioisotope decay in meteorites	Cosmogenic theory of element formation Galactic evolution Time of flight (red shift)

of millions of years can be calibrated in this fashion with clocks based on the reliable solar day or solar year: so can the accumulation of sediments that make rock, the recession of the moon's orbit away from the earth: and so can the velocity of light. Calibration in the time dimension bears a close resemblance to distance calibration in astronomy where all scales are based on terrestrial triangulation.

Man counts his days by marking the passage overhead of the sun and stars. He lists these days on calendar pages to make years and centuries. As long as records are kept continuously, an unbroken baseline of time results. The trouble is, many different kinds of calendars have been kept by different civilizations over the 6000 years of recorded time. Although the length of the year may be roughly the same in Mayan, Egyptian, and modern calendars, little else is. The real problem, however, is not in how many days one puts in a week, a matter of esthetics, but in relating the ancient calendars to modern calendars. How is a specific year on the ancient Chinese calendar related to the day you read this? Happily, many floating dates can be tied down through records of eclipses and other astronomical phenomena that can be seen the world over. By keeping track of how many times the earth swings around the sun we can construct a satisfactory, if limited, foundation for time measurements. Even this time baseline varies—no two years are identical. Today we remedy nature's inconsiderate vagaries with atomic clocks; but in looking far backward there is no choice except to assume that the length of the years has been fairly constant for 6000 years.

During this period, many geological and astronomical clocks have advanced a measurable amount, enough, at least, so that we can judge how rapidly the hands on these clocks turn in terms of modern years. Submerged Roman ruins of known age enable us to attach time scales to the encroachment of the sea in that part of the world. The accumulation of silt in river estuaries gives us clues to how long it took to build geological formations.

As our interest in time expands from days to centuries to billions of years, larger and larger baselines are constructed upon the basic unit, the solar day.

When geologists measured the thicknesses of strata and correlated the earth's complex covering of sediments, they quickly realized that the earth was many millions of years old instead of the few thousand allowed by the Jewish calendar or even the two million estimated by the ancient Chaldeans of Mesopotamia. By 1900, scientists accepted the fact that even a billion years might not be sufficient for the earth to have cooled, solidified, and evolved into its present state. The earth's mantle was a crazy quilt of distorted rocks that yielded pieces of history here and there. Underlying strata obviously preceded covering rocks (a geological hierarchy in time), but no key to absolute dating of the distant past appeared.

Happily for the timekeepers, Henri Becquerel discovered radioactivity in 1896. This was the key to bring order from disorder. Radioactive decay, in which unstable nuclei spontaneously change into new nuclei, proceeds unchanged by temperature, pressure, or chemical environment. Geologists quickly seized this gift from the physicists. As early as 1913, a quantitative geological time scale based on measurements of natural radioactivity was published by A. Holmes in England. Today, radioactive dating techniques have tagged human remains only a few thousand years old as well as the oldest rock ever found by geologists. This ancient rock base is found on the Kola Peninsula (near Murmansk), in the Soviet Union, and is about 3.4 billion years old. By measuring uranium's decay rate for a few hours, geologists build clocks that reach back to the time when rocks first permanently solidified on the seething surface of the molten earth, but, as we shall see, not prior to that geological milestone.

By all standards, radioactive clocks are the thing to use in geochronology. The only immutable thing about a radioisotope is its half life. Uranium-238, for example, has a half life of 4.5 billion years. For every gram that originally solidified in a rock sample, we would expect to find a half gram left 4.5 billion years later, and a quarter gram left after 9.0 billion years. In practice, though, we cannot tell how much uranium was actually trapped in a given rock. What we really measure in a rock sample are the amount of uranium-238 remaining and quantity of lead-206: the latter is the stable byproduct of the decay of uranium-238. If lead-206 was present at the moment of solidification, the time scale will be distorted. Similarly, if any of the uranium and lead diffused away or got carried away by chemicals over the geological eons, accuracy will suffer.

Thus, radioactive clocks, which advance their hands at such constant rates, may not tell the right time because the hands move in front of a distorted scale of numbers. To illustrate the type of problem encountered, consider again the decay of uranium-238 into lead. At one stage in the chain of decaying radioisotopes that culminates in stable lead-206, the radioactive gas radon is formed. Being a gas, it can diffuse away through the rock before decaying

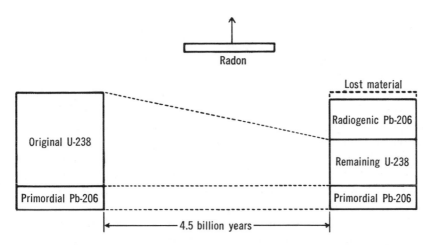

In 4.5 billion years half of the U-238 in a sample rock has decayed into radiogenic Pb-206 and radon.

into lead-206; erroneously low ages result. Early radioisotopic age estimates of the earth came up with a figure close to two billion years, less than half of that estimated today. Part of the problem was the diffusion of radon gas. As geologic ages marched by, natural catastrophes introduced further sources of error. Molten rock obviously releases radon and can separate the parent radioisotope (U-238) from its stable daughter (Pb-206). Remelting and metamorphic activity grossly distort age measurements.

One of the bulwarks of the scientific method is the scientists' insistence on measuring the same things in different ways. If the answers are different, there is no rest until the sources of error are found. Happily, there are many other radioisotopes with long half

lives occurring naturally in the earth's rocks that can be used to
check each other. Here are some of the most important:

PARENT RADIO- ISOTOPES	STABLE DAUGH- TER(S)	HALF LIFE (BILLIONS OF YEARS)	APPLICABLE MINERALS AND ROCKS
U-238	Pb-206	4.50	Uraninite, monazite, zircon, black shale
U-235	Pb-207	0.71	
Th-232	Pb-208	14.10	
Rb-87	Sr-87	47.0	Muscovite, biotite, K-feldspar, le-
K-40	Ar-40	1.3	pidolite, glauconite
	Ca-40		Muscovite, biotite, glauconite

Historically, the group of three radioisotopes heading the table
is the most important. These are the isotopes with which A. Holmes
and A. O. C. Nier, two pioneer geochronologists, worked. In addition to their frequent and simultaneous appearance in terrestrial
rocks, these isotopes have different half lives, and this permits some
degree of internal self-checking. A piece of granite, for example,
may contain all three parents, all three stable lead daughter isotopes, plus primordial lead-204, which has resided unchanged in
the granite since it solidified. The three radiogenic leads (206, 207,
and 208) may also have been present along with primordial lead-
204 when the granite solidified, but their concentrations increased
as their parent isotopes decayed. Careful comparison of the concentrations of all the lead, uranium, and thorium isotopes allows scientists to correct for any lead-206, 207, or 208 that was there in the
beginning.

The rubidium-87 and potassium-40 dating schemes provide still
further cross checks and estimates of corrections to be made for
radon losses by the uranium-thorium-lead clock. Several other radioisotopes, such as rhenium-187 and lutetium-176, yield additional
independent estimates that help bring the numbers on the face of
the clock into clearer focus. Such time-scale concordance proves
vital to estimating the age of the universe as a whole.

Radioactive dating of terrestrial rocks takes us back to about
3.4 billion years. But this is not the total age of the earth—it is only
the age of those solidified rocks that could retain the radioisotopic
clocks. The earth may have existed billions of years in a molten

state before solidification commenced. How do we get at this period of the earth's history? The first way is to calculate how long it would take a molten sphere of primordial earth stuff to cool and form a crust. In making such computation, one conceives of a solid crust— which cannot get rid of heat as well as a circulating liquid surface —being formed and remelted many times until the earth loses enough heat to retain a crust. What is more, the immense quantities of heat that are produced by the radioactive decay of potassium-40, one of our clock components and a relatively common isotope, must be factored into the calculations. When the computer finally clicks out some answers, it seems that at least another billion years must be added to the 3.4 billion measured from solid rocks, making the earth about 4.6 billion years old.

A second kind of clock confirms the cooling computations. If we assume that the meteorites we intercept from outer space each day originated in the same cataclysm that created the earth and that, being very small, instantly solidified, their age should be the same as the total age of the earth. Radioactive measurements have been made, and meteorites do seem to be about 4.5 billion years old. Meteorites are apparently the oldest pieces of material available to us.

The sun, the Milky Way, and the universe must of course be older than 4.5 billion years. From our foundation in geochronology can we possibly find clocks that will help us date astronomical objects that we cannot touch, and analyze them for radioactivity?

Geochronology deals with rock specimens that can be subjected to various analyses in the laboratory. In contrast, the age of the sun must be found from studying remotely the radiation the sun emits. There is no intrinsic property of special lines that is changed by age in the way that recession velocity causes a red shift. We are looking for some solar property that varies in a known way with age and is still detectable at 93 million miles. Astronomers armed with spectroscopes have been active for little more than a hundred years (Joseph von Fraunhofer first observed solar absorption lines in 1814); it is difficult to conceive of any solar property that would change a measurable amount in that length of time and yet be capable of indicating a span of time greater than five billion years. The time ratio is over ten million. In other words, any cumulative solar property would probably not be detectable by us.

The vital clue that leads us out of the quandary is the realization that the history of our sun can be reconstructed by studying other stars. The sun is a typical star belonging to what astronomers call the Main Sequence. Its composition, brightness, and size are pretty much like those of thousands of other stars that have been studied in detail. Through telescopes, then, we can see how the sun must have looked at various stages during its evolution and what its future will be as well. The accepted theory of stellar evolution, which will be covered in detail in Chapter 5, assumes a certain "burning" sequence during which the star consumes the supply of thermonuclear fuel it inherited during its initial formation. By knowing the burning rates, the amount of energy per unit mass of fuel, and the total quantity of fuel consumed, astronomers can calculate how long it takes a star to move from youth through middle age to death. It is like knowing how much gasoline a car carries and how fast the fuel is burned. One can immediately compute how long the car has run by looking at the fuel gauge.

According to stellar evolution theory, our sun is about five billion years old, with a life expectancy of another five billion years. As astronomers are wont to emphasize, the sun is an average, run-of-the-mill, middle-aged star.

So far, our chronology of the universe hangs together pretty well: the earth's age is 4.5 billion, and the sun was probably lit 5.0 billion years ago. Stellar theory also states that many stars seen in the sky are approaching ten billion years. With this background, can we find refutation or substantiation in cosmology? Can we pin down the age of the universe?

We will begin with an old friend. The red shifts of the galaxies are almost universally explained as a Doppler effect arising from their velocities of recession. If we assume that all these galaxies are flying away from a point of origin, say the Big-Bang's holocaust, we can make a time-of-flight estimate of age. That is, if the distance of a galaxy and its velocity of recession are known, that galaxy's age would be given by:

$$\text{age} = \frac{\text{velocity}}{\text{distance}}$$

This assumes, of course, that the velocity of recession has not altered during the galaxy's flight from the source of the explosion.

Edwin Hubble, the pioneer in measuring galactic velocity and distance, generalized his findings by supposing that the ratio of velocity to distance was constant for all galaxies. This assumption also fixes the age of the universe because the Hubble Constant (velocity/distance) is just the desired number. Many subsequent measurements of the Hubble Constant infer that the age of the universe is somewhere between seven billion and twenty billion years. This result is consistent with stellar theory and the radioactive measurements of meteorites, but it is still a rather wide range.

Estimating elapsed time by dividing distance by speed is intuitively satisfying. We do this in our everyday travels. A much less obvious clock for the universe relies upon the statistics of galactic distribution. Assuming that everything did begin with a Big-Bang, we would expect to see a good deal of disorder in the way the galaxies, which are the products of the Big-Bang, are distributed throughout the sky—that is, if the universe is still rather young. An old universe presumably would show many of the irregularities ironed out by the passage of time. It's much like throwing a stone in the water and comparing the initial splash with the orderly ripples that spread out. Statistics and the laws of physics can describe this transition from disorder to order and attach a time scale to the process as well. Unfortunately the method is not very precise because it only tells us that the universe is much older than 0.1 billion years and much younger than 100 billion years. At least the result does not conflict with other independent estimates.

Both the time-of-flight and statistical clocks assume the correctness of the Big-Bang Theory—but, suppose the Steady-State Theory is correct. The age of the universe would then be infinite, and surveys of stars would show them to be all ages from those newly born to those expiring due to old age. This turns out to be true; some seem to be only a few million years old, and some have at least ten billion years behind them. But these observations do not really tell us that the age of the universe is infinite any more than the various ages of people we see on the street tell us that mankind has existed forever. Star lifetimes and human lifetimes cannot reveal how many generations have risen and passed away during the history of the universe, for there is just no way to measure infinity with finite rulers and clocks.

If the Steady-State Theory is eventually substantiated by observa-

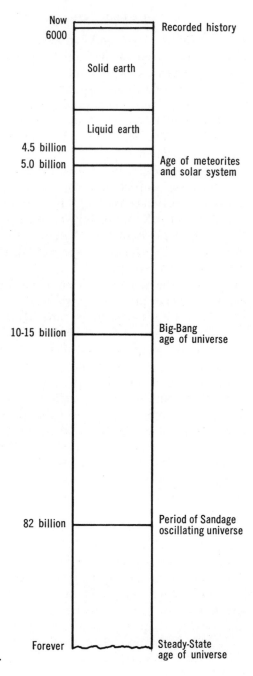

Chart history of the universe.

tion, we will have to accept its claim of a universe infinite in time and extent. Our present age measurements neither confirm nor deny this universe. The Big-Bang Theory, on the other hand, is also consistent with the ages we have found for the earth and stars. In fact, the compatibility approaches confirmation in many minds. The possibility of an oscillating universe also exists, with the condensations being equivalent to a series of Big-Bangs. The astronomer Allan Sandage, who favors an oscillating universe, believes that the Big-Bangs are spaced about 82 billion years apart and that we are now about ten billion years into an expansion phase.

Summarizing, the age of the universe seems to be somewhere between ten billion and twenty billion years. This figure is consistent with all ages we can measure directly and with the Big-Bang Theory and its variants.

Time is a most elusive factor in our existence. It is hard to comprehend the passage of a thousand years, much less ten billion. The farther back we go in time, the harder it is to construct clocks with confidence. The history of time measurements gives us further cause for concern; the antiquity of mankind, the age of the earth, and the age of the universe have all increased substantially as new clocks have replaced old ones. Most people alive today can remember when the age of the earth was reckoned at only two billion years. Today life itself is thought to be older than that; and the earth's age has risen to 4.5 billion. At least today's geological, astronomical, and physics clocks seem to be giving us the same readings; and that is reassuring. The clocks are getting better.

4

CHECKING OUT EINSTEIN

New physical theories advance over the corpses of those they supersede. When Albert Einstein, an obscure junior official in the Swiss patent office, published his Special Theory of Relativity in 1905, the old concepts of how light was propagated through space had already received a death blow at the hands of the American scientists Albert Michelson and Edward Morley. They had shown experimentally—the only convincing way—that the velocity of light was not affected by the motion of its source. The model that died was that of the luminiferous ether.*

The luminiferous ether was conceived by nineteenth century science as an invisible, all-pervading medium that carried light and other electromagnetic waves, much as jelly transmits mechanical vibrations. To most nineteenth century scientists the thought that something (light waves) could be transmitted through nothing (empty space) was abhorrent. Water waves require water, and sound waves, air; therefore, light waves need an ether. The stars and planets cruised majestically through this strange medium that apparently offered no resistance to their progress. The ether was at once essential to those who needed mechanical analogies for natural processes and embarrassing to those who couldn't figure out how a vacuum could contain a solid rigid enough to transmit transverse light waves as water waves transmit up-and-down motion.

* The word *ether* was borrowed from Aristotle's name for the fifth element that made up his cosmos.

The resolution of this conflict took scientists a giant step away from the comfortable science of Newton, wherein most physical things were related to everyday events, such as a falling apple or the ripples on a pond.

The Michelson-Morley experiment, science's most famous experiment-that-failed, was designed to show that the velocity of light measured by a terrestrial observer would be retarded if the light bucked the ether streaming past the earth and increased when it was carried along with it. The experimental situation resembled that of a man on shore trying to measure the speed of a boat moving up and down a flowing river. Actually, Michelson had first tried the experiment alone in 1881 while he was studying at the laboratory of Hermann von Helmholtz in Berlin. That experiment failed to show any velocity changes. In 1887 Michelson and Morley constructed a better instrument (an interferometer) at the Case School of Applied Science in Cleveland. The result was still negative; no matter which direction the light traveled through the "flowing ether" its velocity was the same to the earth-anchored observer. Or almost the same. Very slight differences were noted, but they were much smaller than would be expected if the earth actually sped through the ether as it orbited the sun at twenty miles/sec. Morley and an associate, Dayton Miller, repeated the 1887 experiment several times between 1902 and 1904 with identical results.

Miller, in particular, could accept neither the answer given by his apparatus nor the concept of relativity supported by his experiments. He continued to look for the ether and in 1921 claimed that he had found evidence of ether drift in his measurements of light's velocity. His work, however, was found to be invalid. Scientists keep repeating the Michelson-Morley experiment—most recently using lasers—and they keep getting the same negative results. Apparently, within experimental error, the velocity of light does not depend upon the motion of the light source. The ether model died at the turn of the century, but some gravediggers still try to resurrect it either because they cannot stomach relativity or (more interestingly) because the results have not been *completely* negative. Most scientists today assume a totally negative result and many modern theories depend upon this interpretation.

Einstein should not be blamed or praised for the idea of relativity. It has been around for at least a hundred years. Poincaré formulated a relativity theory in 1899 and extended it in 1904. He claimed that it was impossible to determine the absolute motion of a physical body, inferring that all motion is relative. In fact, Poincaré and Hendrik Lorentz, a Dutch physicist, built so much of the Special Theory of Relativity that some scholars refuse to associate Einstein's name with it. What Einstein contributed in 1905 was a precise and generalized statement of Special Relativity. He

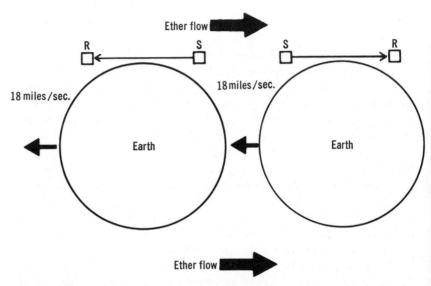

The Michelson-Morley experiment showed that the velocity of light between source S and receiver R was unchanged by the direction of flow of the postulated ether. This experiment dealt a crippling blow to the ether hypothesis.

then went on to General Relativity, which he built largely with his own hands.

The postulates of Special Relativity are two:

1. The laws of physics are identical in all inertial (unaccelerated) frames of reference.

2. The velocity of light is independent of the motion of its source.

The second postulate is simply the fact of the Michelson-Morley experiment. The first postulate is a broad generalization of experience. If, by way of illustration, you drop a ball to the floor of a train moving at constant velocity, it will fall in the same straight line you observe when you drop it in your living room. But consider what happens outside your own frame of reference. If you could see that falling ball through the train windows from a station platform, it would seem not to fall in a straight line. In fact, Special Relativity predicts that that ball should not only fall on a slant line but also appear heavier than it is when the train is not moving. The ball should also seem squashed in the direction of the train's motion. Furthermore, a clock on the same train would seem to run more slowly to the observer on the platform. These predictions from the two postulates of Special Relativity are not part of our common-sense low-speed experiences at all; they are discernible only at velocities approaching that of light. No known instruments could measure that ball's minuscule mass increase on a train rushing past at 60 mph, so that Special Relativity does *not noticeably* contradict our common sense in *ordinary* situations.

In the following three sections, some of the more interesting (and sticky) aspects of Special Relativity will be described. In particular, *measurements* of these unexpected effects will be emphasized, because only measurements can confirm or deny the postulates of Special Relativity and the models of the world we build around them. After that, we shall tackle General Relativity, which baffles our common sense even more.

In 1895 physical scientists were smug. They believed that they had physics pretty well under control. True, the ether problem was still a thorn in their sides but no doubt it would soon be plucked out as science steam rolled on. The thought that mass might increase with velocity would have been received with the ridicule reserved today for UFOs. Yet, by 1905, merely ten years later, the Special Theory of Relativity was formulated, stating that the mass of an object approached infinity as it approached the velocity of light. To throw that comfortable world into real confusion, Max Planck had just promulgated the quantum theory and Henri Becquerel had discovered radioactivity. The monolithic temple of Newtonian science was cracking and showed signs of complete collapse.

Scientists immediately looked for something that moved at speeds close to that of light in order to measure its mass and see if the predictions of the Special Theory were borne out in reality. The

Special Theory predicts that mass varies with velocity in the following way:

$$m = \frac{m_0}{\sqrt{1 - \dfrac{v^2}{c^2}}}$$

where: m = the mass of the object in question moving at velocity v, as measured by an observer in reference frame No. 1, say a physics laboratory;

m_0 = the mass of the same object at rest;

c = the velocity of light (186,000 miles/second).

As v approaches c, m increases rapidly toward infinity.

Physical reality in this case is not everyday physical reality because our unaided senses see nothing traveling at near-optic velocities. The physicist, though, with his ordinary senses augmented by detectors of atomic particles, such as the Geiger counter, can accelerate protons and electrons in particle accelerators to speeds where relativistic effects can be "seen." Let us say that the physicist accelerates electrons down a long evacuated tube with electrostatic fields. Special Relativity predicts that these electrons will be harder and harder to accelerate as they approach the velocity of light because of their increase in mass. The increasing sluggishness of electrons in such accelerators is a well-known fact. No matter how much force is applied, the electrons get harder to push. At 99% of the velocity of light, an electron behaves as if its mass had increased by a factor of seven. To the physicist trying to accelerate them, this mass increase is real—and frustrating, too. Special Relativity is clearly confirmed by this particular experimental fact.

If you substitute a high-speed spaceship for the electron and watch it zip past the earth at 0.99c, it would seem to you, an earth-based observer, that the spaceship responds to the pull of earth's gravity as if it were indeed seven times more massive than you know it to be. The spaceship pilot, however, would notice no mass changes in himself or his ship, but it would seem to him that the earth's mass had increased by a factor of seven. It all depends upon where the observer sits. It's all relative.

Special Relativity also predicts that fast (i.e., high velocity) clocks should run slower. This idea is completely ridiculous because time moves on imperturbably like a steady universal river. Newton said this about time: "Absolute, true, and mathematical time, of itself, and by its own nature, flows uniformly on, without regard to anything external." The reliability of time was a rock upon which he built his concept of the universe. Relativity, though, revealed a fickle time that varied with velocity. The precise degree of fickleness is specified by the following equation:

$$t = t_0 / \sqrt{1 - v^2/c^2}$$

where $t = $ time on the moving reference frame as measured by the "fixed" observer;
and $t_0 = $ time in the fixed reference frame.

Checking out this prediction of Special Relativity took some ingenuity since no one knew how to hurl conventional watches at nearly the speed of light. Fortunately, nature provides some natural watches: radioactive particles that disintegrate in half lives (t_0) that can be measured accurately in the laboratory. These half lives should be longer (t) if the particles are moving at near-optic velocities.

The particle chosen to play the role of a clock is the mu-meson, or "muon" for short, a subatomic particle that decays spontaneously into other particles with an average lifetime of about 2.2 millionths of a second. Rather than create the muons artificially and then try to accelerate these ephemeral particles to high speeds before they disappear during decay, a natural source is put to work. Cosmic rays, when they bombard the earth's atmosphere, interact with atoms in the high atmosphere and generate a flux of muons. As muons shower down on the earth, their number decreases the farther down they penetrate because more and more of them disintegrate as they travel. Scientists in balloons, surface laboratories, and deep mine shafts measure the numbers of muons intercepted at various altitudes. The results show that the high-velocity muons do not disintegrate as fast as one would expect from lifetime measurements of stationary mesons created in terrestrial laboratories. The increase in lifetime, in fact, is roughly that predicted by the Special Theory of Relativity. Time stretching or "dilation" at relativistic velocities is an experimental fact. Special Relativity is again confirmed. Once more, the experimental situation is far removed from everyday experience, but the equations still reduce to commonsense experience at the low velocities to which we are accus-

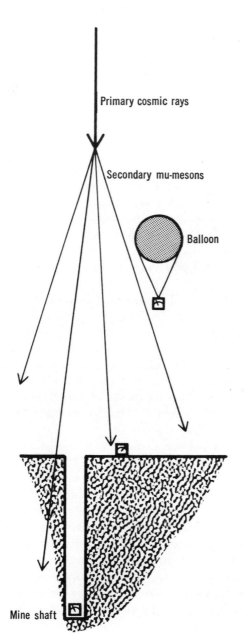

Primary cosmic rays

Secondary mu-mesons

Balloon

Mine shaft

Time dilation predicted by Special Relativity is demonstrated by mu-mesons that decay in flight to earth from point of origin in high atmosphere. Detectors in balloons, on the surface, and in mines indicate that the average lifetime of the mu-meson is "stretched" by virtue of its high velocity, but only when viewed by a stationary observer.

tomed. In other words, we couldn't measure any changes on planes and trains.

The Sunday supplements have described how future astronauts returning from trips to Alpha Centauri at high speeds will have aged less than their earthbound contemporaries. This trick for cheating time is called the Twin Paradox. Superficially, the logic seems sound: the clock carried by one twin in the speeding rocket ship will undeniably run more slowly than a similar clock left back on earth with his brother. It also seems reasonable to assume that a biological process such as aging will slow down as the days are stretched out by relativistic time dilation. Speed would then be a fountain of youth for astronauts, enabling them to fly to the stars and back within their lifetimes. Returning to earth still young, they might find their grandchildren in their declining years. The tale is a good one for the Sunday supplements, but there is a hitch. Special Relativity applies only during those periods when the spaceship is moving at constant velocity with respect to the earth. In order to make a round trip to a distant star, the spaceship must first accelerate to near the speed of light and decelerate at its destination. The same events occur on the return leg. Special Relativity cannot be applied to round trips, which, by necessity, must include changes of course and other accelerations. Thus, no paradox exists. If we insist that our astronauts remain youthful during interstellar oydsseys, perhaps we should install deepfreeze units in preference to relying on relativistic time dilation.

Besides, Special Relativity insists that there is no preferred frame of reference. The star-bound astronaut in the Twin Paradox can just as validly consider himself to be at rest and the earth to be moving. In his estimate, his terrestrial twin would not be aging as rapidly as he.

Special Relativity seems to tell us that two objects cannot collide with a relative velocity greater than that of light. Relative velocity is a matter of simple addition. If you are standing by the roadside and clock two cars on a collision course at 60 mph each, they will surely crash at a relative velocity of 120 mph. Similarly, if you walk into a physics laboratory and aim two electron guns at each other and start firing electrons at each other at 0.9c, the electrons will collide at 1.8c according to laboratory instruments. Or, you can shine two flashlights at each other and have confidence that the photons course past each other at a relative velocity of 2c. Our common sense cannot quarrel with such observations.

Special Relativity provides us with a formula for adding velocities that unfortunately has led to many misinterpretations. The culprit equation is:

$$V = \frac{u + v}{1 + \frac{uv}{c^2}}$$

where: $V =$ the velocity of an object in a moving inertial frame as measured *in a stationary inertial frame;*

$u =$ the velocity of the object as measured by instruments *in the moving inertial frame;*

$v =$ the velocity of the moving inertial frame as measured by instruments *in the stationary inertial frame;*

$c =$ the velocity of light.

The misinterpretations always arise when u and v are taken as relative velocities, when they are actually measured by different instruments residing in different inertial frames.

In studying electrons bearing down on each other at a relative velocity of 1.8c, does the scientist measure any velocity exceeding c in the laboratory? The answer is no; each electron travels at 0.9c. If we attach a reference frame to one of the moving electrons, would an "observer" sitting on the electron see the other electron bearing down on him at 1.8c? The answer again is no, which is another jolt to our common sense. But, since no one has really accumulated a fund of common sense while riding high-speed electrons, common sense might be expected to be deficient here. The formula for adding velocities can also be used here:

$V =$ the velocity of the approaching electron as measured by the observer now sitting on the first electron (note the switch of reference frames);

$u =$ the velocity of the approaching electron as measured in the old stationary reference frame which was 0.9c;

$v =$ the velocity of the old stationary reference frame as seen by the observer sitting on the electron (here, v = 0.9c).

Substitution in the equation gives:

$$V = \frac{1.8c}{1.81}$$

In other words, the observer astride the electron sees the second electron approaching at a velocity just under that of light. What you measure depends upon where you are sitting, and in no case will you ever measure the velocity of a material object to be faster than that of light.

We must bear in mind that the Special Theory is only a *theory*, a model, if you will. Tomorrow, some scientist may make a measurement that conflicts with what the theory predicts. If other scientists repeat the experiment and confirm the contradiction, consensus will repeal the theory and a search will be made for a better one. The Special Theory, however, is a keystone in the physicist's model of the universe. Despite its departures from common sense, it has been checked exhaustively and no discrepancies have yet been found. The word "yet" is significant because history shows that *all* theories ultimately bow to better ones. There is no reason to believe that the Special Theory will forever properly describe everything we measure, particularly as science probes deeper into the atomic nuclei and farther out into space.

By 1913 Einstein's classic trio of 1905 papers on Special Relativity, Brownian motion, and the photoelectric effect had carried him from his job at the Swiss patent office to the University of Zurich and then to a special chair created for him at the Kaiser Wilhelm Physical Institute in Berlin. Because he was a Jew, the ascent from clerk to Herr Professor had been slow. Finally, though, he was able to devote his life to science.

He published his General Theory of Relativity in 1916. With only pencil and paper Einstein inspired a whole army of experimenters, mainly astronomers who chased eclipses around the world and scrutinized the sun and Mercury for the effects he predicted. It was a classic tale of science. Einstein had formulated a new law of gravitation; in most physical situations, however, General Relativity Theory reduced to Newton's Theory. Einstein thoughtfully specified three places where measurements might show his theory superior to Newton's 300-year-old law of gravitation. These "exceptions" have occupied the thoughts and efforts of two generations of experimentalists:

The measured advance of the perihelion (the orbital point closest to the sun) of Mercury is 43 arcseconds per century greater than that predicted by Newton's law of gravitation.* This was an observational fact known to Einstein before he announced his General Theory, causing some detractors to claim Einstein constructed the General Theory in such a way as to explain this discrepancy. Nevertheless, without any outward appearance of contrivance, Einstein's General Theory predicts a result very close to that measured today. Some modern scientists, such as Robert H. Dicke, suggest that Mercury's orbital discrepancy can be accounted for by the rotationally flattened shape of the sun.

Starlight passing close to the sun would be deflected an arcsecond or two, just as if photons possessed mass. This effect—completely foreign to Newtonian mechanics—has been observed during every total eclipse since 1919. Einstein's reputation was on the line when the Royal Astronomical Society of London sent eclipse expeditions to northern Brazil and Principe Island (off West Africa) in 1919. If no light deflection had been measured, the General Theory would have been buried by the anti-Einstein forces that were waiting in the wings for such an opportunity.

The force of gravity retards photons leaving a body like the sun, creating a gravitational red shift. This effect has been observed with white dwarf stars, but recent tests using the Mössbauer Effect (described later in this chapter) have been more convincing.

The famous equation $E = mc^2$, stating the equivalence of energy (E) and mass (m), also evolves from General Relativity. So does the well-publicized concept of curved space.

The General Theory that led to the conceptual unification of mass and energy also synthesized time and space into a four-dimensional space-time continuum. One feature of General Relativity appeals strongly to the artist in the theoretical physicist. This is the Principle of Covariance. In essence it states that the laws of nature take the same mathematical forms in all conceivable coordinate systems. The mathematical expression of the law of gravitation, for example, would be identical in two reference frames in relative motion. This touches the soul of the theorist who is trying to describe nature in the most general, most accurate, and most esthetic terms. To him,

---

* During the 1890s Asaph Hall, an American astronomer, pointed out that this discrepancy could be explained by replacing R^2 in Newton's law of gravitation by $R^{2.0000001574}$.

the Principle of Covariance possesses symmetry, which is certainly one aspect of the beauty that is one goal of the physical theorist.

No discussion of gravitation and relativity would be complete without the mention of Ernst Mach and the Baron von Eotvos. Both men figured prominently in the work leading up to Einstein's Principle of Equivalence; that is, the assertion that gravitational and inertial mass are identical. The Principle of Equivalence is basic and critical to General Relativity. Let us see what it means and how it might be experimentally tested.

First, what does the principle mean in terms of experiments? To use Einstein's famous example, someone in a closed, windowless, and freely falling elevator would believe himself weightless. He could not distinguish between free fall and the absence of gravity that he would encounter if taken into deep space far from any star. Conversely, the inertial forces created by a rocket attached to the hypothetical elevator in gravity-free space could not be distinguished from gravity itself. Today's satellites make it seem obvious that inertial mass, acted on by centrifugal force, can be precisely balanced by gravitational mass, which pulls the satellite off the straight trajectory it "wants" to follow into an ellipse.* Unfortunately, satellites are subjected to a slight air drag, solar radiation pressure, and other forces that make them poor instruments for checking the Principle of Equivalence.

To many, it must seem that trying to prove the Principle of Equivalence is making the world unnecessarily complicated. Mass is mass, and that's all there is to it. But there are some subtleties to be discovered by the man who looks deeply enough. Ernst Mach, the Austrian physicist who gave his name to the Mach Number, was such a man. Mach swam straight against the mainstream of science, denying the atomistic viewpoint and opposing relativity, even though he contributed much to the latter. Mach's principle is typical of his thought-provoking contributions to the philosophy of science. Mach believed that inertia—that reluctance of mass to move in response to an applied force—can be ascribed to the collective grav-

---

* In a circular orbit, gravitational force balances centrifugal force: $GmM/R^2 = mv^2/R$, where G = the Universal Constant of Gravitation, m = the satellite mass, M = the mass of the earth, R = the radius of the orbit, and v = the satellite's velocity. There is a temptation to cancel the m on each side of the equation even though the left m is gravitational mass and the right m is inertial mass.

itational pull of all the matter in the universe. Wouldn't any object be reluctant to move if held by springs attached in all directions? The mass or substance of an object is thus not intrinsic but instead dependent upon the surrounding universe. If, for example, the mass of the universe were not uniformly distributed, inertia itself would be different in different directions.

Mach's principle has such a deep hold on cosmologists that a number of experiments have been performed to determine whether inertial mass is the same when forces are applied in different directions. So far, no one has found it easier to push a brick in one direction than another. Still more fascinating is the implication that the expanding universe, with its recession of gravitating bodies, leads to a progressive weakening of the force of gravity here on earth. In retrospect, Mach's principle gave Einstein much food for thought while he was formulating the General Theory, but it remains only partially assimilated.

Now for an experimental test of the Principle of Equivalence. The Hungarian physicist Eotvos was the first to test the principle with high precision. Using a very sensitive torsion balance, Eotvos was able to establish that inertial mass (as in the equation for centrifugal force) and gravitational mass were equal within one part in 10^8 (i.e., 100 million). Eotvos' results, published in 1890, gave physicists confidence that the m's in their equations were at least numerically equal if not of the same substance. The Eotvos experiment has been repeated many times with more sensitive equipment. Inertial and gravitational mass have now been shown to be equal to within a few parts in 10^{10} (10 billion).

Most tests of the general theory have depended upon ultra-precise astronomical measurements, such as the slight warping of light rays passing the sun during an eclipse and the red shift of photons trying to escape the sun's gravitational field. The trouble with astronomical measurements is that the effects are so small that they are apt to get lost amid background noise or distorted in physical processes beyond our knowledge or control. Until recently, the astronomical tests of General Relativity were reassuring, but not precise enough to cause all scientists to enthusiastically embrace the theory. What was needed was a terrestrial test that anyone could perform without waiting for eclipses or having to worry about excessive noise and distortion. The "perfect" experiment came with the discovery of the Mössbauer Effect by Rudolph Mössbauer at the Max Planck Institute at Heidelberg in 1957.

Mössbauer found that the gamma rays emitted by radioisotopes incorporated in crystals will, under certain conditions, be very nearly identical in energy. A crystalline absorber containing the same radioisotope will, in effect, be tuned to these mono-energetic gamma rays, providing it is motionless and on the same horizontal plane. A gamma-ray detector mounted behind the absorbing crystal will show this resonant absorption of the gamma rays under these conditions. But the least relative motion of the source

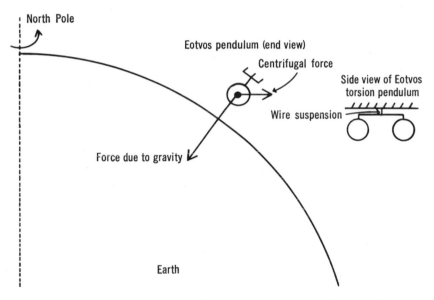

In testing the Principle of Equivalence with the Eotvos balance, the axis of the balance is lined up in an east-west direction. Each ball feels the pull of gravity and centrifugal force. As a result, the balance does not hang exactly vertical, and there are horizontal components of both forces that will exert a net torque on the balance if inertial and gravitational mass are not equal. This torque would be counterbalanced by the twisted suspension wire. The balance is then rotated exactly 180°. The direction of restoring torque in the wire remains the same, but the direction of torque due to any unbalanced forces reverses. The pendulum bar, therefore, would not rotate exactly 180°, if the Principle of Equivalence did not hold.

or absorber will detune the experiment due to the Doppler effect. Furthermore, orienting the experiment in a vertical plane will detune it because the gamma rays will be retarded by gravity (according to General Relativity) as they travel upward toward the absorber. A red shift results.

The Mössbauer Effect was first used to check the General Theory's

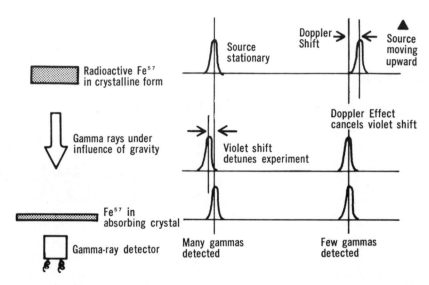

Checking gravitational violet shift with Mössbauer Effect. Fe^{57} gamma rays are shifted toward higher wavelengths by gravity so that they readily pass through absorber. Doppler Effect achieved by slowly raising source retunes experiment so that most gammas are absorbed.

prediction of a gravitational red shift by the English scientists J. Schiffer, T. Cranshaw, and A. Whitehead in 1960. Using iron-57 as the radioisotope gamma-ray source, they caused the gamma rays to "fall" through a few meters onto the absorber and in the process be accelerated by gravity like a dropped baseball. (See above.) This positioning of absorber and source made this a violet-shift rather than a red-shift test of the General Theory. Just the few meters of separation caused significant detuning of the experiment. Resonance was restored by the slight downward motion of the absorber, so that the Doppler effect just canceled the gravitational effect. The calculated violet shift was within about one per cent of that predicted by the General Theory. This simple and elegant experiment has provided the best and most convincing check on the General Theory.

Both Special and General Relativity are mathematical models of the universe that offer us few mechanical means to help visualize what is really going on. At least the Newtonian universe possessed stars and planets that moved in ways we could understand. Unhappily, the universe revealed by modern instruments does not lend itself to easy mechanical interpretations.

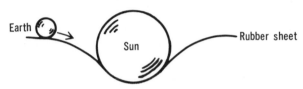

In General Relativity, one may think of the presence of mass-distorting space-time—shown here as a two-dimensional rubber sheet rather than the undrawable four. It is the warping of space-time by the presence of mass that pulls the earth toward the sun in this view of nature. The "heavy" sun pulls the earth toward it because it distorts space and time rather than exerting some mysterious force across 93,000,000 miles of vacuum.

There is, however, one easily visualized aspect of General Relativity that was quite popular with science writers in the 1920s and 1930s. This was (and is) the possible curvature of space, a quality of the relativistic universe with a geometric appeal. In General Relativity, the presence of mass warps time and space. Visualize the four dimensions of time and space in the vicinity of the sun as a two-dimensional stretched rubber sheet, with the sun as a heavy sphere depressing a portion of that sheet. A smaller mass would be "attracted" to the sun, not by virtue of gravitation but rather because space and time are distorted. Even the path of light would be bent by the curvature of space/time near the sun. The Newtonian concept of a universe occupied by moving centers of gravitational force is replaced by a four-dimensional continuum where objects and light rays move along paths (called geodesics) dictated by the structure of space/time. In this vision of the cosmos, space is flat if a light ray on the average moves in a straight line. Space possesses positive curvature if the light ray ultimately circles back and intersects its starting point. You can visualize the whole universe confined to the surface of a soap bubble. Light would travel along the film and return to its point of origin. In negatively curved space, light rays would bend but never come back on themselves.

Einstein originally believed that the universe was static and with positive curvature such that a light ray would complete a circuit of the universe in some two hundred billion years. This was all before the discovery and acceptance of the expanding universe. The Dutch astronomer William de Sitter, who did much to promulgate Einstein's work, quickly saw that the general recession of the galaxies, as inferred from their red shifts, meant that the radius of curvature for the universe was steadily increasing. Einstein was eventually convinced that this view was the correct one.

All modern cosmologies predict that space has some positive curvature. The question is how much? The curvature of space is measured by counting the number of galaxies per unit volume and a function of distance from the earth. If the number of galaxies per unit volume decreases with distance, space has positive curvature. If an increase is measured, space has negative curvature. Present counts indicate a positive radius of curvature equal to about 13 billion light years and increasing as the galaxies recede.

Special Relativity and General Relativity have had profound effects on philosophy, even though scientists are reluctant to apply relativity beyond those physical things they measure. Newton's science has been described as materialistic. To him all matter moved according to immutable laws. These laws could be projected far into the past or future, depending upon the number one substituted for time in the equations. While the solid rock of Newtonian science remained intact, there was little room left for fate, free will, and those who wished to be captains of their souls. The advent of relativity was thus hailed by some as a shift away from materialism, possibly because it hinted of secret worlds that our everyday senses could not penetrate. At one point, the Soviets considered relativity so much a threat to materialism that they labeled it a "reactionary" theory and warned that espousal of it was undesirable political conduct.

On the other hand, relativity has been criticized as dehumanizing science and divorcing our descriptions of nature from our natural referents of color, shape, and size. Indeed, General Relativity in the 1940s was portrayed by journalists as so abstract and complicated that only a dozen scientists besides Einstein himself even understood it. The fact is that relativity always reduces common sense situations to common sense terms. Relativity isn't foreign; it applies in the kitchen and laboratory alike; it predicts strange effects only in a few extreme situations seen by a few physicists and astronomers. As for the philosophical interpretations of relativity, philosophers have been wont to believe in relativity only when it supported their personal views of the cosmos.

Today, Special Relativity is an accepted, well verified brick in that Temple of Science that was partially demolished and rebuilt by Einstein, Becquerel, and Planck and others. Einstein put only the finishing touches on Special Relativity. It was a theory that had to evolve. The pieces to the puzzle were mostly available, just as they were when Newton synthesized his law of gravitation from Kepler's laws.

General Relativity, however, is another matter. Experimental checks support the theory as far as they go. Except for the Mössbauer test, the tests could be more precise. There are only a very few places where General Relativity predicts different results from Newton's law of gravitation and the differences are slight. Besides the experimental difficulties, solution of the equations of General Relativity are extraordinarily troublesome. Results so far are either very approximate or so restricted in scope that they are not too helpful in understanding the real world. Then, too, there are philosophical problems, such as the relevance of Mach's principle. Nevertheless, almost any physicist will say that he has confidence that the General Theory of Relativity gives us the best available description of the universe. The General Theory has conquered little by little. We find it hard to comprehend the violent opposition that boiled up around it during its first two decades of life. Max Planck, whose quantum theory encountered similar resistance, had an appropriate remark: "A new scientific truth does not triumph by convincing its opponents and making them see the light, but rather because its opponents eventually die, and a new generation grows up that is familiar with it." *

* Quoted from "Scientific Autobiography," Max Planck.

READING LIST

BARNETT, L. *The Universe and Dr. Einstein*, William Sloane Associates, New York, 1957.

BERGMANN, P. G. *An Introduction to the Theory of Relativity*, Prentice-Hall, Englewood Cliffs, 1942.

————. Relativity, *McGraw-Hill Encyclopedia of Science and Technology*, McGraw-Hill Book Company, New York, 1966.

BONDI, H. *Relativity and Common Sense*, Doubleday and Company, Garden City, N.Y., 1964.

BRIDGMAN, P. W. *A Sophisticate's Primer of Relativity*, Harper & Row, New York, 1962.

EINSTEIN, A. *The Meaning of Relativity*, Princeton University Press, Princeton, 1956.

GAMOW, G. *Gravity*, Anchor Books, Garden City, N.Y., 1962.

MC VITTIE, G. C. *General Relativity and Cosmology*, University of Illinois Press, Urbana, 1965.

5

HOW A STAR WORKS

We see the stars only as pinpoints of light rising in the east and setting in the west. Among the thousand or more visible to anyone who cares to watch them carefully from season to season some are bright, some less so. Some seem reddish, some blue. They can be grouped to outline gods and constellations; they form the Southern Cross, the Big Dipper, and the "little eyes" of the Polynesian navigators. They move slightly over the centuries but follow no systematic paths. What more can be said about the stars? Not much, from what we see with the naked eye; a great deal more, if we use telescopes and spectrometers. The analysis of starlight is the subject of this chapter. With the aid of our repertoire of earth-verified physical laws and the meager evidence brought to us by photons filtered down through our atmosphere, we can mold models of stars millions of light years distant.

For two thousand years astronomers could say little beyond the obvious fact that there were a good many stars out there. In 134 B.C. Hipparchus, greatest of the ancient Greek astronomers, was startled to see a bright star (a nova) where none existed before. Stimulated by this apparition in the supposedly immutable heavens, he constructed the first systematic star catalog. Hipparchus listed the coordinates of about a thousand stars and divided them into brightness categories. The twenty most brilliant were of the "first magnitude," while those just visible to the naked eye were assigned to the sixth magnitude. Cataloging the stars was a beginning, but a list alone revealed no more about nature's inner workings than a stamp collection does of nuclear physics. No system or grand plan showed through the voluminous columns of numbers.

Hipparchus' catalog received a few additions from Ptolemy in the second century after Christ. A star catalog with 1022 entries was contained in Ptolemy's famous *Megiste Syntaxis* or "greatest composition." After the fall of the Roman Empire the Arabs acquired, translated, and preserved Ptolemy's catalog as *Al Magisti*, from which our title *Almagest* is derived. The *Almagest* remained a cornerstone of astronomy for nearly a thousand years. No one, however, was able to extract any secrets from it. It was just another list.

With the invention of the telescope around 1600, the number of "seeable" stars multiplied many times. But before order could be made out of the thick jungle of new observations, astronomers had to find stellar characteristics more meaningful than brightness and location in the heavens. Ideally, a theorist seeking an end to the chaos of unrelated measurements would ask at least for stellar distances, masses, velocities, and something less subjective than "magnitude" and "brightness." This was a tall order for an observational science being developed under a pall of gases that obscured most of the spectrum.

Astronomers, however, made up for these handicaps with ingenuity. A distance scale was constructed first, using triangulation for the nearest stars, with the earth's orbital diameter of 186,000,000 miles as a baseline. (See Chapter 1.) A German accountant-turned-astronomer, Friedrich Wilhelm Bessel, announced the measurement of the distance to the star 61 Cygni, in 1838. It was eleven light years away; an incredible distance that suddenly made the universe seem a much larger place. Bessel was followed by other interstellar surveyors. Among them was Miss Henrietta Leavitt, who constructed the Cepheid-variable distance scale in 1912, while at the Harvard Observatory. Chapter 1 relates how this new scale carried distance measurements out to the edge of our galaxy.

Just knowing the distance to a mysterious object does not enlighten us about the object itself. The successful measurement of distance after centuries of attempts is, however, an essential ingredient to a grand generalization we are slowly approaching.

Certainly, one of the more important stellar attributes is "brightness" or, as astronomers call it, "magnitude." Hipparchus had already assigned the thousand-plus stars he saw to magnitudes 1 through 6. His telescope-armed successors over the centuries enlarged his catalog by many thousands of entries. The discovery that stars resided at varying distances from the earth forced scientists to call the magnitudes they measured "apparent magnitudes," because a very bright star might seem dim only because it was far away. Attenuation with distance had to be eliminated and "apparent magnitude" converted to "absolute magnitude" by correcting for distance. All stars had to be measured on the same basis if an overall pattern were ever to be seen.

The first step in putting stellar magnitudes on a truly scientific basis was taken by Karl Schwartzschild, who eventually became the first director of the Göttingen Observatory. Early in this century, Schwartzschild measured the degree that photographic film was blackened by the images of the different stars. This gave him a number, or "photographic magnitude," for each star that all astronomers could reproduce at will. Astronomers could now replace the highly subjective, 2000-year-old "visual magnitude" with hard numbers measured on a uniform basis throughout the world. Soon, the photoelectric cell and other light-measuring devices came along, and the discipline of stellar photometry was born.

Careful photometry showed that some of Hipparchus' first magnitude stars were considerably brighter than other first magnitude stars. Revamping the scale of apparent magnitudes involved a two-way stretch; the uncounted dim stars seen only through the telescope had to be assigned magnitudes greater than six, if the scale of Hipparchus was to be preserved, the stars brighter than reference stars of magnitude 1 had to be assigned numbers smaller than 1— even negative numbers. By agreeing that a difference of five magnitudes means that one star is one hundred times brighter than another, astronomers brought the magnitude scale under control. The bright star Sirius, for example, has an apparent magnitude of −1.4, while the sun's is −26.7. The faintest stars yet detected are of the +23rd magnitude.

All absolute magnitudes are figured by supposing that the star is a distance of 10 parsecs away. (One parsec equals 3.26 light years.) Sirius, only 2.7 parsecs away, has an absolute magnitude of

+1.5, compared with its apparent magnitude of −1.4. The sun turns out to be a rather feeble star on an absolute basis, standing at +4.9 on the absolute scale.

At last a measure of stellar brightness existed that was independent of distance from earth and free from the idiosyncrasies of individual observers. Even so, knowing that some objects are big and others small does not identify the constituents that make them work. The next step in stellar diagnosis required a special kind of surgery, but not of the cutting kind.

To plumb the insides of the stars, men turned to the spectrometer (or spectroscope). The spectrometer uses a glass prism or ruled grating to disperse light into its constituent wavelengths. Since the wavelengths of light emitted by a source or absorbed in transit reveal the identities of the atoms and molecules involved, the spectrometer is a valuable tool for analysis at a distance. Actually, spectrometers see only that radiation that "leaks" out to the stellar surface and escapes absorption by the thick stellar atmosphere. The wavelengths emitted by hydrogen dominate many stellar spectra. Hydrogen, then, must be a major constituent of many stars. Each star has a different spectrum, yet there are many similarities. Astronomers first sorted out stars according to "spectral type," almost as arbitrarily as Hipparchus had assigned his 1000 stars to six bins according to magnitude. The stars showing the strongest hydrogen lines were classified as A-type; those with slightly weaker hydrogen lines were B-type; and so on down the alphabet. It was intuitively satisfying to be sorting out the stars according to some physical property other than brightness. But even though the alphabet was orderly the rationale behind the assignment of letters was not.

Clarification came with the understanding that the *temperature* of the stellar surface was an all-important factor in determining which spectral lines were bright. Eventually, the confusion was straightened out and spectral categories were laid out according to increasing temperature. Just as Hipparchus' magnitude scale was stretched as astronomy became more scientific, so the alphabet was distorted by the new classifications. The *Draper Classification* (named after the American spectroscopist Henry Draper) employs the letter sequence, O, B, A, F, G, K, M, R, N, S, which arranges the stars by descending temperatures. (Quite naturally, college students found the letters mnemonically irresistible and immortalized the sequence with: *Oh, Be a Fine Girl, Kiss Me Right Now, Smack!*) The spectral category definitions are now much more precise and specific. For example, A-type stars now possess spectra showing strong hydrogen lines (as before); ionized magnesium and silicon lines; ionized calcium, iron, and titanium lines begin to appear here; helium lines are absent.

When *The Henry Draper Catalog* was published at the turn of the twentieth century, astronomers had before them a list of 225,000 stars, giving both magnitudes and Draper classifications. Absolute magnitude was a measure of a star's intrinsic brightness, while the Draper classification indicated its temperature range. Each star in the catalog thus had two dimensions; perhaps now someone would perceive a generalization that would tie the hundreds of thousands of cataloged stars together with a common bond.

The grand synthesis was discovered independently by two uncommunicating, geographically separated scientists—as is so often (and so strangely) the case in matters of discovery and innovation. In 1905 and 1907, the Danish astronomer Ejnar Hertzsprung published reports in a semi-popular German photography periodical. In these reports, he pointed out that absolute magnitude and spectral classification are *related*. That is, if the two parameters are plotted one against the other on a sheet of graph paper, a pattern emerges. Most stars fell within a band Hertzsprung called the "Main Sequence." Hertzsprung's discovery gathered dust, unread by the scientific fraternity for several years. In 1914, Henry Russell, director of the Princeton University Observatory, rediscovered the "sequence" found by Hertzsprung. Today, the Hertzsprung-Russell Diagram (see below) boasts many more points, each representing a star; but the additional data only confirm what Hertzsprung and Russell found more than a half century ago: that there is some connection between absolute magnitude and spectral classification.

In itself, a Hertzsprung-Russell Diagram reveals no startling new physical truth. It is only a convenient and intriguing way of organizing stellar properties, but the diagram makes us think, and that is what is important. It is like trying to understand the movements of ocean waves by studying ripple patterns in the sand.

A scientist expects nature to be orderly; and the Hertzsprung-Russell Diagram is a manifestation of order. The diagram itself, however, was *not* the model of a star, nor did it tell how stars worked. It was only a hint, a superficial indicator of underlying orderliness and reason behind the universe.

The Hertzsprung-Russell Diagram points the way to a stellar model. It says (implicitly) that stars are different, but in a *continuous* way; that is, there are no embarrassing gaps in the diagram's Main Sequence and stars grade smoothly from one spectral type to another. What could be more natural than to think of the Main Sequence as a "river" of stellar evolution, with stars being born at one end and dying at the other? Logic reinforces our notions here, because the stars are energy sources that are kindled with finite fuel supplies. Ultimately fuel runs low, the flame dims, and the star pops off one end of the Main Sequence to be seen no more. Now, stellar models had not only to account for the Hertzsprung-Russell Diagram but they could also be tested by it.

Taking clues from the sun, our nearest star, the model of a star on the Main Sequence should consist of an incandescent ball of gases that

—Falls within the confines of the Main Sequence so far as spectral type and absolute magnitude are concerned.
—Obeys all the physical laws established on earth, such as the conservation of energy, Newton's law of gravitation, and so on.
—Possesses a long-lived source of energy and, in addition, some way of getting internal heat to the surface where it can be radiated away.
—Has an age consistent with the age of the universe.

Creating such a model is quite a feat, considering the fact that astronomers can watch stars only from great distances during lifetimes that are negligible when compared to a star's.

The best place to start building a star model is with the energy source. The mainspring of a star must be a prodigious power source. Before the discovery of energy-rich thermonuclear reactions, scientists were very much at a loss to account for stellar energy production. In 1854, Hermann von Helmholtz, the German physicist, considered the possibility that the gravitational potential energy of a contracting star might be the stellar mainspring. His computations quickly showed that a star like our sun would burn itself out in just a few million years with such a feeble source of power. The geologists needed one hundred times that time span for their historical model of the earth. Lord Kelvin and other scientists calculated their way to the same paradox. Energy sources known before

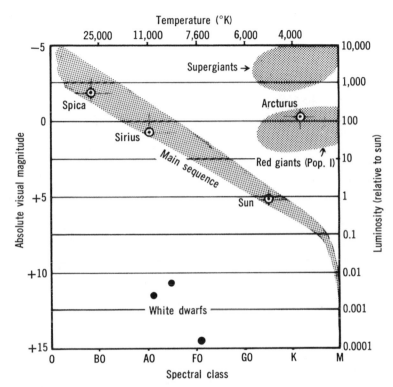

Each point on the Hertzsprung-Russell Diagram represents a star. Most measured stars are either on the Main Sequence or the red-giant region. The sun is located on the Main Sequence between spectral classes GO and K.

1900, such as the "fossil" fuels, would not have sustained a star's life (most specifically, the sun) for the time needed by the geologists.

The first clue to the resolution of this paradox came in 1931 when an Austrian physicist, Fritz Houtermans, and a British astronomer, Robert Atkinson, joined forces to see whether or not some nuclear reaction might keep the sun's pulse beating long enough to satisfy the geologists. Radioactivity had been discovered some 35 years before, and rapid developments in nuclear physics since then had shown that four hydrogen nuclei were heavier when separated than when united in one helium nucleus. Houtermans and Atkinson reasoned that if they could somehow "cook" hydrogen nuclei so that four of them fused into a helium nucleus, the excess mass would be turned into enough energy to make hydrogen an ideal stellar fuel. George Gamow, in his book *A Star Called the Sun,* relates how Houtermans and Atkinson originally titled their classic paper "How to Cook a Helium Nucleus in the Potential Pot." Their work was soon published in the journal *Zeitschrift für Physick,* but with a less engaging title. Due to the lack of precise experimental data, Houtermans and Atkinson could specify no particular chain of nuclear cookery, but they did identify the most prominent stellar fuel (hydrogen) and its "ashes" (helium).

The next chapter in the story began in 1938, but with a more familiar cast and stage: two geographically separated scientists working simultaneously but not in touch: Hans Bethe, in the United States; and Carl von Weizsacker, in Germany. Both men discovered that the nucleus of carbon can serve as a high-temperature catalyst in "cooking" hydrogen into helium. More precisely, carbon would help begin the synthesis of helium, but when the nuclear construction work was complete, the carbon would be released unaltered and ready to begin a new round of synthesis. This was the famous "carbon cycle" that made the newspaper front pages just as World War II was beginning. It had popular appeal because "cycles" were familiar to everyone from the work of biologists with the oxygen and carbon dioxide cycles in the earth's biosphere. While Bethe and von Weizsacker were working out the details of their carbon cycle, Charles Critchfield, a young American physicist at George Washington University, discovered another hydrogen-to-helium fusion reaction that succeeded at lower temperatures. In this reaction two hydrogen nuclei fuse directly—without any catalyst—to form a nucleus of heavy hydrogen. Further fusions with other hydrogen nuclei created the helium nucleus. The Critchfield fusion reaction, called the H-H reaction, was originally thought to be of minor importance in stellar energy production because of the improbability of several successive fusions of hydrogen nuclei. More refined calculations, however, showed just the opposite. For two decades, the carbon cycle and H-H reaction were in and out of first place, reminiscent of a close pennant race in baseball. Nowadays, the carbon cycle is believed to be dominant in the hotter stars, while on cooler stars, such as the sun, the H-H reaction prevails.

Nuclear fuel generates about 100,000 times as much energy as the best chemical fuels in terms of weight consumed. Even so, the sun "burns" some 600,000,000 tons of hydrogen each second. About ninety-nine percent of this hydrogen is fused into helium; the rest is converted directly into the energy that keeps the sun (and us) alive. Fortunately, the sun is so huge that even at this rate of fuel consumption there is enough hydrogen to last at least five billion years more.

The identification of hydrogen as the primary stellar fuel had a profound effect on theorists' attempts to build a stellar model. Any model would have to include huge quantities of hydrogen fuel and in addition show how to kindle the thermonuclear fires. How could ignition temperatures of millions of degrees be reached without the benefit of nuclear heat? Lord Kelvin, von Helmholtz, and others had discovered one kind of stellar match in the late nineteenth century when they looked at gravity as a possible source of stellar energy. They found the match, while Bethe, von Weizsacker, and Critchfield found the fuel. Stellar conflagration would commence when an immense cloud of interstellar gas and debris contracted into a dense, spherical mass under the influence of gravity and turned the kinetic energy of inwardly rushing atoms into heat. Hydrogen nuclei would begin to fuse—via the low-temperature H-H reaction at first—and soon nuclear fire would be hot enough to keep itself going without gravity's match. A star would be stable when the contracting effects of gravity were just offset by the tendency of the hot gases to expand. When the hydrogen fuel was consumed, the star was finished and seen no more. It was a neat, tidy model—as far as it went.

Physical models that seem sound may conceal gross violations of natural laws behind a facade of reasonableness. Deeper probing of the model suggested above shows no such overt contradiction of natural laws, but still there are unanswered questions that make the model a little shaky.

The idea of gravitational sweeping-up and concentration of miscellaneous interstellar matter into a star-size mass or "protostar" holds no hidden perils for the theorist. Neither do thermonuclear ignition and the subsequent "burning" of hydrogen to helium at the star's hot center. But how does the heat from a star's core get out to the surface through many thousand miles of dense ionized gas? If the heat doesn't work its way out of the core in some way, ex-

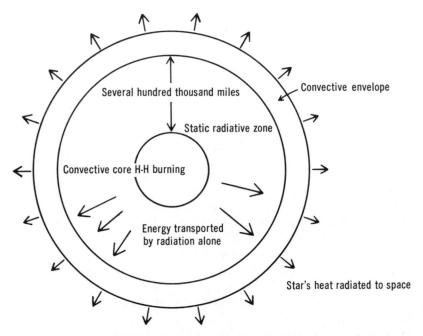

Model of a Main Sequence star of moderate mass. All heat is generated in the convective core by the H-H process or the carbon cycle. Energy passes through the static, radiative zone by a process of X-ray emission and absorption. At the star's outer surface, all energy is radiated away.

plosive instability results. In fact, all the ingredients for a colossal H-bomb seem to be present.

The current model of an average Main Sequence star proposes three zones: inner and outer convective zones, where there is considerable mixing of gases; and a thick, non-convecting "radiative" zone between them, through which heat passes mainly by means of radiation. The key to draining off the heat from the hot central convective zone, where the bulk of the H-H burning occurs, is *heat transfer by radiation*. Without it, stars would explode as soon as they are formed, for our familiar heat-transfer processes of conduction and convection are completely inadequate over distances of thousands of miles from star center to surface.

Energy transfer in the stellar model looks like this: almost all energy is generated in the central core at temperatures of tens of millions of degrees. Thermal radiation at these temperatures is in the X-ray region and is therefore very penetrating. X-rays from the core invade the static radiative zone where they are absorbed only to be quickly reemitted as new, slightly less energetic X-rays. Through a series of successive absorptions and reemissions, the X-rays carry energy from the core to the outer convective zone, where the energy is finally radiated away into space. The thick, radiative zone is actually relatively *transparent* to thermal radiation in the X-ray region of the spectrum.

The three-zone model is also stable in time. The outward forces created by radiation pressure tend to balance gravity, which tends to compress the star still further. A stable condition exists if the stellar core generates more energy than could be transported to the surface and radiated away. When energy loss is less than energy production, the star core temperature first rises, increasing the outward radiation pressure and causing core expansion. When the core expands, it is cooled and thermonuclear energy is generated more slowly. Conversely, if the star is being cooled at its surface faster than the core is generating energy, the core cools and contracts. Gravitational energy is pumped into the star during contraction and the hydrogen fuel nuclei come closer together. The net result is that energy generation rises. The stellar model thus automatically adjusts itself so that all energy generated is radiated without any catastrophic explosion.

Stability is a transitory thing in nature. Even stars have to die sometime, though they may live billions of years. The above model really represents a "snapshot" of an average-size star, such as the sun, taken during middle age while on the Main Sequence of the Hertzsprung-Russell Diagram. No one, especially a scientist, is satisfied with just a few frames from the middle of a movie. Past history must be reconstructed and the future predicted for complete satisfaction; and the successful stellar model must journey intact through time for us without stretching our credulity.

History on the Hertzsprung-Russell Diagram begins at the right as the protostar forms swiftly from coalescing gases. The surface temperature rises and the protostar becomes luminous. Moving to the left as its temperature increases, the track of a medium-size star makes a fishhook-shaped trace as it settles down to its place of residence on the Main Sequence. The bigger the mass of the protostar, the higher the temperature it reaches before outward radiation pressure balances inward gravitation. Initial position on the Hertzsprung-Russell Diagram is therefore an indication of initial mass. Bigger stars are hotter and start life farther up and left on the diagram. Protostars trace out their "fishhooks" of youth in just a few million years—only an instant compared to the billions of years they will spend on the Main Sequence. Because the protostar stage is ephemeral, the Hertzsprung-Russell Diagram catches few stars in the act of entering the Main Sequence and is therefore almost blank in these areas.

After a few billion years, a Main Sequence star begins to develop a fuel shortage in the inner convective zone. Plenty of fuel exists outside in the radiative zone but it is static and can't get into the region of high temperature where it can "burn." The stage is set for further motion on the Hertzsprung-Russell Diagram, which by now has become a most useful roadmap in time. The road from here on, however, is the subject of much controversy. In fact, the farther we travel into a star's old age, the rougher the journey. Some theorists claim that no passable roads have yet been built. One thing is certain, the notion introduced earlier comparing the Main Sequence to a "river" in time is untenable. In youth and in age, stars stray far from the Main Sequence.

The concentration of stars in the red-giant region of the Hertzsprung-Russell Diagram suggests an old-folks' home for stars leaving the Main Sequence. After all, they possess considerable fuel outside their cores and still must have some zip lift. Red giants are, as the name implies, cool but large and rarefied. They are so large that they appear bright despite their low surface temperatures. They quite properly accumulate at the upper right of the Hertzsprung-Russell Diagram. The stellar model has revealed nothing so far about red giants; their sizes and temperatures are not compatible with the hot nuclear core idea. If they do not arise from protostars directly, where do they come from? Perhaps a bridge exists between the red giants and the Main Sequence.

One such bridge was built by George Gamow and Charles Critchfield in 1939. This bridge is a useful and seemingly quite sturdy extension of the widely accepted model of a Main Sequence star. Suppose, argued Gamow and Critchfield, that after a Main Sequence star had cooked all its core hydrogen into helium, its core contracts, converting gravitational energy to heat, until the temperature at the edge of the formerly static radiative zone reaches about twenty million degrees. Thermonuclear fusion of hydrogen will renew at the boundary. Then, the reaction might proceed outward, burning hydrogen and leaving helium behind as it progresses. In essence, Gamow and Critchfield suggested a switch from a burning core to a burning shell. Inside the burning shell, only inert helium would remain. In this view, the outer portions of the star would be heated to higher temperatures than those existing when the star was on the Main Sequence. The star would swell to a tremendous size and its outmost layers would drop in temperature. The shell-like burning zone would still be producing prodigious quantities of power, but the star's immense external surface could easily radiate it away at temperatures lower than the star possessed on the Main Sequence. The time track of the star on the Hertzsprung-Russell Diagram would thus bend up to the right and intersect the red-giant region. There the star would reside, growing ever larger as the burning shell zone approached the stellar surface.

Incidentally, Gamow and Critchfield encountered serious computational obstacles in their search for the bridge between the Main Sequence and the red giants. With hand computers, they could only show a "tendency" for stars to leave the Main Sequence in the rough direction of the red-giant region. When electronic digital computers became available, more detailed computations confirmed the existence of the bridge.

Following a star's time track out of the red-giant has been more difficult. When the hydrogen fuel in the star's outer regions has been consumed, must it die out and become cold and inert? Perhaps not; because even helium can be burned thermonuclearly if the temperatures are high enough. The dotted time track shown in the figure leads down toward the white-dwarf region of the diagram. This is where many astronomers believe the graveyard of the stars to be. Eventually, even a white dwarf cools down, and the star moves to the right, off the Hertzsprung-Russell Diagram, its journey ended.

The stellar model portrayed above has much to recommend it.

No physical laws are violated; the life-death cycle is intuitively satisfying; the stellar ages are compatible with the time desired by geologists and cosmologists for their theories; and the whole tale is quite in keeping with the Hertzsprung-Russell Diagram. For those who still doubt, there is additional supporting evidence. For those who believe too confidently, there are some embarrassing unexplained problems.

It is tempting to say that the Hertzsprung-Russell Diagram supports the stellar model just described. Of course it does. The model was specifically designed to "explain" ("conform to") the diagram. If it did not, it would never have reached a place in scientific literature. Good, independent tests of the model are scarce.

One notable success of the stellar model under scrutiny concerns the matter of stellar age. The model states that the larger stars enter the Main Sequence farther to the left, and that they are bigger and hotter than their smaller brethren. Because they are bigger and hotter they consume their fuel at an extravagant rate and appear to age faster. Sure enough, the study of globular clusters of stars, in which all stars seem to have been born at the same time, shows that the bigger stars in the cluster begin to stray from the Main Sequence first. The smaller stars are not so wasteful with their fuel and remain on the Main Sequence longer. This observation strongly supports the model.

The stellar model is far less successful in explaining what happens to the more massive stars—those more than twice the mass of the sun—after they leave the Main Sequence. The problem is that the Hertzsprung-Russell Diagram seems to offer them no place to go. The smaller stars move to the upper right and become red giants; but there are very few red supergiants on the Diagram for the big Main Sequence stars to aim at. They must go somewhere, but no one knows where for sure. Whatever does happen, happens fast; otherwise there would be a few stars captured in transit on the Hertzsprung-Russell Diagram to show the fate of the large Main Sequence stars.

Confidence in the model can be shaken further by considering the problems of novae and supernovae, those colossal stellar explosions that have startled astronomers for millennia, and by the deviant stars that are too rare to be noticed on the Hertzsprung-

Russell Diagram but too frequent to be completely ignored, particularly the variable and pulsating stars. The model might be called
inarticulate on these points. Possibly this is so because the model
wants only further development and refinement. Theorists armed
with computers are rapidly exploring all ramifications of the model.
Only computers, for example, can tackle the job of tracing the paths

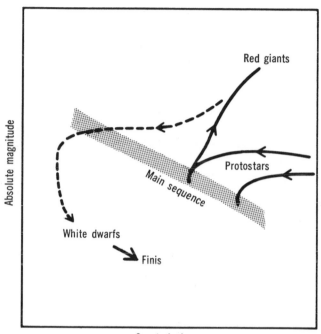

Spectral class

Time tracks on the Hertzsprung-Russell Diagram. The path leading out
of the red-giant region toward the white dwarfs is a subject of controversy.

of a whole series of stars with different masses as they burn up their
core of hydrogen and begin to depart the Main Sequence.
    In contrast to the cosmological battlefield which resounds with
competing models, the stellar arena holds but one major contender
describing the early evolution of a star. After a star's sojourn on the
Main Sequence variations of the model proliferate, but they all are

built on the same foundation. New experimental evidence, when it appears, may contradict the present model. If the Main Sequence features are untenable, the whole theory of stellar evolution will be in complete disarray. There are no widely recognized alternative models.

New experimental evidence is most likely to come from the space program. Large satellite observatories, such as the OAO (Orbiting Astronomical Observatory), permit astronomers to measure stellar spectra at wavelengths in the far ultraviolet and the infrared, which do not penetrate the earth's atmosphere. Infrared surveys of the sky, for example, could catch cool protostars in their rapid flight from the right edge of the Hertzsprung-Russell Diagram to their resting place in the Main Sequence. A few infrared "snapshots" like this would strongly support the current stellar model. Ultraviolet spectrometers carried aloft by sounding rockets have already uncovered several perplexing facts during their brief flights. The few stars observed during such flights radiate less ultraviolet light than the current model predicts. Some stars also seem to be surrounded by peculiar ultraviolet clouds or "nebulosities." These discoveries naturally bother astronomers a great deal because they tend to undermine confidence in their one and only tenable model. Most OAO experiments have understandably been assigned to the ultraviolet region of the spectrum. Rockets have also discovered many X-ray sources in the skies. Explaining a star emitting copious X-rays may strain the model to the breaking point because there is no place on the Hertzsprung-Russell Diagram for stars with surface temperatures so hot that they emit mostly X-rays.

A likely development when astronomical satellites open up the observable spectrum is the discovery of something entirely new and unexpected—something that theory with its model never dreamt of. Whole new areas of the Hertzsprung-Russell Diagram may be filled in with stars that are unseeable from earth because their radiations are absorbed by the atmosphere. New discoveries make life difficult for the theorist, and the continual recasting of models may seem confusing and dismaying to the layman looking for hard answers and explanations. The fact is that astrophysics is on a frontier where the Indians are far from pacified. A theorist is always in danger, but that is what makes the whole business exciting.

READING LIST

ABETTI, G. *The History of Astronomy*, Abelard-Schuman, New York, 1952.

GAMOW, G. *A Star Called the Sun*, The Viking Press, New York, 1964.

GLASSTONE, S. *Sourcebook on the Space Sciences*, D. Van Nostrand Company, Princeton, 1965.

INGLIS, S. J. *Planets, Stars, and Galaxies*, John Wiley & Sons, New York, 1961.

LEY, W. *Watchers of the Skies*, The Viking Press, New York, 1963.

McGraw-Hill Encyclopedia of Science and Technology, McGraw-Hill Book Company, New York, 1966, entry on "Stellar Evolution."

6

THE SOLAR SYSTEM'S
ELEVEN-YEAR PULSE

The ancient Greek astronomers held the sun to be a perfect, un-blemished sphere of fire. It sailed across the sky once a day, im-maculate, immutable, and apparently oblivious to the earth's re-actions.

We know today that the sun's surface seethes with tempests tens of thousands of miles across, and that the solar "winds" reach across hundreds of millions of miles to buffet the earth and the other planets. The earth's weather, the price of wheat, the number of fox skins turned in by Canadian trappers, innumerable factors of earth life seem to beat in synchronism with the solar pulse.

It is a fascinating cause-and-effect story. The sun's storms spew out radiation and hot ionized gases that bombard the earth, jiggling magnetometers and lighting our polar skies with auroras. The phys-ical model of the cycle of solar-terrestrial relationships introduced here is a fairly sophisticated one, but it says nothing about *why* the sun has an eleven-year cycle.

Two independent lines of research, geophysics and solar physics, were found to be linked together by interplanetary forces.

The scientific discipline of solar physics took centuries to mature because the much-too-influential Greek philosophers had declared that the sun was perfect and unchangeable. Why waste time watch-ing something that never changed?

Far to the east, the Chinese had not heard this pronouncement from Hellas and recorded "birds" flying in front of the sun as early as 28 B.C. Westerners, who really could not miss seeing sunspots with the naked eye, thought little about them until the seventeenth century. They reasoned that, because religion and philosophy asserted that the sun was unblemished, those "spots" must be planets or vapors passing between the earth and sun.

In the reign of Charlemagne a great black spot was seen on the sun by the people of France for eight consecutive days. The scientists of the time—if they could be so called in the eighth century—claimed the spot was the planet Mercury. This was not a bad guess since Mercury does cross the sun's face on occasion—but it makes the passage in just a few hours.

The invention of the telescope placed the spots where they should be—on the face of the sun. Although Galileo was apparently observing sunspots through his telescopes as early as 1610, the German astronomer Johannes Fabricius (surname Latinized from Goldschmidt) was, in 1611, the first to publish results of sunspot observations. A third telescope-using solar observer of the period was Father Christoph Scheiner, who worked at Ingolstadt, in Upper Bavaria. Scheiner ran head-on into the Aristotelian dictum of the immaculate sun when his ecclesiastical superiors assured him that either his telescope or his vision was faulty. Galileo drove to the heart of the matter. In a 1612 series of letters commenting on the observations of Fabricius, Galileo thoroughly described the irregular shapes of sunspots, their continual formation and dissolution, and their regular march across the face of the sun. Most importantly, he stressed that sunspots were *surface* phenomena and not stars or permanent bodies.

Having found the sun infected with a kind of pox, scientists were hard put to account for the imperfections. Kepler stated in 1613 that the spots' variability suggested clouds but that terrestrial analogies would probably not be of much help. It took 250 years more for men to realize that the sun was in reality a huge thermal machine with a complex, turbulent surface. Sunspots are only the most obvious visible manifestations of solar activity.

Before examining the inner workings of sunspots, their cyclic changes must be discussed. The periodic nature of sunspot behavior led to the cause-and-effect association of solar and terrestrial events.

When two objects are separated by 93,000,000 miles, there must be some observable "bridge" if event A on the sun is to be associated with event B on the earth. The earth-sun bridge was built on the evidence of similar synchronous solar and terrestrial cycles.

The early observers of sunspots believed that they were irregular, unpredictable, and unlikely to lead to any new understanding of nature. The discovery of their cyclic nature came from an unexpected source. Heinrich Schwabe was a German pharmacist with an amateur's passion for astronomy. Casting about for some astronomical project to occupy his free daytime hours, he hit upon the idea of carefully watching the solar disk to see if he could catch a new, undiscovered planet as it sped across the bright image. Schwabe began his project in 1826. When new planets failed to materialize, he became preoccupied with sunspots. On every sunny day for seventeen years he sketched, with infinite patience, the ever-shifting pattern of spots he saw on the sun's face. By 1843 he had concluded that the number of sunspots increased and decreased in a ten-year cycle. His discovery was generally ignored as happenstance or suspect data from an unreliable source. Nevertheless, the discovery had been made and remained a part of the scientific inheritance for someone else to pick up and use.

While most nineteenth century astronomers were looking for new planets, geophysicists were busy studying earthquakes, volcanoes, and weather in the lower atmosphere. The influence of solar activity on these grosser elements of our environment is negligible save, perhaps, for the weather. The effects of solar activity on weather were buried for centuries in a conglomeration of unsystematic, uncoordinated data. Although an Italian drought in 1632 was associated with the lack of sunspots, this seemed to be a case of blaming the weather on a convenient scapegoat.

The linking of solar and terrestrial effects depended not only on recognizing that there might be some physical bridge other than gravitation but also upon the *systematic analysis* of some facet of the earth's environment that was *strongly* and *directly* affected by the sun. No one was looking for a geophysical phenomenon with this description. Astronomers and geophysicists talked very little with one another until the turn of the twentieth century. Science was fortunate to learn about the effects of the sun on the earth as early as it did.

The vital clue leading to the sun-earth bridge lay in the sun's powerful influence on the earth's magnetic field. A Scottish-German astronomer, Johann von Lamont, director of the observatory at Munich, observed a ten-year cycle in his records of daily magnetic compass needle variations. His geophysical measurements came quickly to the attention of two other astronomers: Alfred Gautier in Geneva, and Rudolf Wolf in Zurich. They realized that this ten-year geomagnetic cycle coincided with Schwabe's suspect ten-year sunspot cycle. Wolf followed up the lead and wrote to many well-known scientists in an attempt to gather sunspot data earlier than Schwabe's. The first public connection of solar and magnetic activity came from still another quarter on March 18, 1852, when Major General Edward Sabine submitted to the Royal Society a report based on magnetic measurements he had made in Canada. The title was "On Periodical Laws Discernible in the Mean Effects of the Larger Magnetic Disturbances." The Sabine report was not published immediately and its title was unlikely to catch the eye of an astronomer. Eventually Wolf received Sabine's report in Zurich and began a detailed study of the sunspot cycle. When Wolf announced that the average sunspot cycle was $11\frac{1}{9}$ years long,° the Scottish astronomer John Allen Broun maintained that this was incorrect because the magnetic cycle period was only 10.45 years and the sun *had* to follow suit. Broun thought that the earth could control solar events.

Humans seem fascinated by correlations, for somehow correlating one thing with another seems to explain both. Sabine's report was the beginning of the most incredible spate of associating related, somewhat-related, and completely unrelated phenomena since the first astrologers divided the heavens up into the zodiac. It seemed that just about everything could be tied to the sunspot cycle; and this was almost as satisfying as making the sun immutable and immaculate was to the ancient Greeks.

The first correlations were reasonable enough. In 1870, Professor Elias Loomis of Yale associated magnetic storms, the number of auroras observed, and sunspots. Today's science can usually explain cause and effect in these cases, but in 1870 it was a complete mystery how the sun could reach across nearly one hundred million miles and jostle the earth's magnetic field and kindle the auroras.

° Actually, the cycle has varied from seven to sixteen years in length.

The study of tree rings soon indicated that trees grow faster during sunspot maxima; wheat prices are also lower, reflecting an abundant harvest. Evidently, there exists some yet undetected solar stimulus that causes plants to grow faster when spots speckle the sun. It may be that rainfall is heavier. The Italians were exceedingly perceptive in 1632 when they blamed the lack of sunspots for their drought. George Gamow, in his book *A Star Called the Sun* tells how the number of lynx and fox skins bought by the Hudson's Bay Company is high when there are lots of sunspots. Perhaps, Gamow says, with part tongue in check, it is because the auroras are brighter then and afford the trappers a better chance of success during the long polar nights.

Stranger still is the observation that sunspot maxima are roughly synchronized with the French and Russian revolutions, both world wars, and the Korean conflict. Fortunately, there were few sunspots during the Cuban missile crisis. Cycles have even become the tools of cultists. In the 1910s and 1940s, it was great sport to tie the stock market and even the future of the world to cycles. Cycles displaced Nostradamus for a while. Undoubtedly there are many subtle connections between earthly and solar events that we cannot yet discern or are too prejudiced to accept. If the sun can stimulate tree growth, possibly, as Shakespeare said, there *is* a tide in the affairs of men— an eleven-year tide.

Just what constitutes solar activity and how can it affect the earth across empty space? In the terminology of this book, what is the current *model* of solar-terrestrial interaction?

Beginning with the sunspots themselves, in the eighteenth century they were believed to be dark mountain tops poking through the sun's photosphere when the "tide" of luminescent material was low. This is an interesting terrestrial analogy that shows the primitive nature of solar physics in those times. Next came the idea that sunspots were holes in the photosphere. This guess was much closer to modern views, except that the sunspots are now known to be "dark" only in comparison with their extremely bright surroundings. Instead of being holes in the photosphere showing the "dark" solar surface underneath, the spots are actually cooler, but still relatively bright areas embedded in the photosphere.

A sunspot begins life as a small, dark *pore* "only" 1500 miles or so in diameter. Within a few days it becomes a full-fledged spot, with maximum development reached in the next week or two. An average sunspot displays a diameter of about 30,000 miles (*four times the diameter of the earth*). A large spot may spread out over the sun's surface for 80,000 miles. Large spots sometimes persist for three months before shrinking and fading away; small spots measure their lives in days. In physical appearance, the average sunspot shows a dark center called the *umbra* surrounded by a grayish rim area called the *penumbra*. A single spot looks very much like a hole in

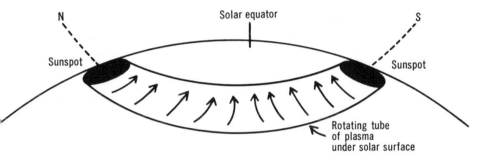

One possible sunspot model. The rotating plasma tube creates the two cool, dark sunspots shown in opposite solar hemispheres. The rotating tube also creates magnetic fields of opposite polarity, as required to explain observations.

the photosphere, and it is easy to understand some of the early misconceptions. Their gross appearance also reminds one of vortices or whirlpools in a turbulent liquid. This may be some sort of optical illusion, but it has inspired several vortex models of sunspots, one of which we will describe shortly.

It is not the individual sunspot but the collective behavior of sunspots that supplies us many clues about their origin. Sunspots usually form groups with as many as one hundred spots of different sizes in a large group. Such a group may be strung out for 200,000 miles across the face of the sun. The sun's visible diameter is 865,000 miles, so that a large sunspot group would extend across one quarter of its face and be easily visible to the naked eye.

Other collective features of sunspot activity give hints about their nature and origin. On the average, sunspots seem to occur in equal numbers and at almost the same times in the northern and southern hemispheres of the sun. Pairs equidistant from the solar equator are common. Any sunspot model must explain this symmetry. Intuition, for example, suggests that pairs of sunspots traveling together across the sun's face might be tied together underneath the visible surface of the sun. Another collective feature of sunspots is their motion left to right across the face of the sun; this is due, of course, almost entirely to the rotation of the sun about its axis. More peculiar is the appearance of new spots at high latitudes during the beginning of the solar cycle and the appearance of new spots at low latitudes toward the end of the cycle. Often the spots of a new eleven-year cycle will begin forming while those remaining from the previous cycle are still in residence near the equator. The sunspot cycle then is not cleancut, like day and night; two cycles may overlap in time.

The more facts uncovered about the sunspot cycle, the more mysterious the whole business seems. Purely visual studies of sunspots have yielded little insight and must be supplemented with other data before even a crude model can be shaped. The tool to apply is the spectroscope.

When the sunspot spectrum is spread out for study, it shows much stronger molecular absorption lines than the adjacent unspotted portions of the sun. This observation supports the belief that the sunspot is cooler than the surrounding bright photosphere because it is high temperature that destroys large molecules. This interpretation is reinforced by the corresponding weaker emission lines from atoms in the sunspot. The sunspot's lower temperatures do not stimulate as much radiation from atoms with high excitation energies. The spectroscope does not suggest that a sunspot is formed from different basic materials than the rest of the sun. It is just cooler. This factor alone is of little help in unraveling the sunspot mystery.

A major contribution to spectroscopy came in 1896 when the Dutch physicist Pieter Zeeman discovered that strong magnetic fields cause spectral emission lines to split into several parts. The degree of splitting is actually a measure of the strength of the magnetic field. Doubling of some of the sunspot emission lines had been noted around the middle of the nineteenth century. In 1908 the American astronomer George E. Hale associated these observations with Zeeman's discovery. Hale's measurements of emission-line splitting showed that the magnetic field associated with a sunspot could be as high as 3000 gauss or more. This figure was extremely high compared to the sun's average surface field of about one gauss and the half-gauss field at the surface of the earth. Even more startling were the polarities of the sunspot magnetic fields; they were opposite for each member of a sunspot pair. What is more, polarities reversed with each new generation of sunspots. Sunspot *bipolarity* was now added to sunspot pair symmetry, lending support to the supposition that pairs are somehow connected to one another by some subsurface structure running under the solar equator because north magnetic poles do not exist without connecting south poles.

These are the major facts to use in constructing a sunspot model, but most solar physicists will admit that no one has been able to put them together in a very convincing way. The explanation of the physical structure of sunspots seems to lie in the relatively new science of *magnetohydrodynamics,* or *MHD.* MHD endeavors to describe the motion of highly ionized, electrically conducting gases called *plasmas.* Being electrically conducting, plasmas are strongly affected by magnetic fields and can be captured and contained in *magnetic bottles* in terrestrial laboratories. Plasmas in motion, on the other hand, create magnetic fields of their own, just as electricity flowing in the windings of an electromagnet generates a magnetic field. At the temperature of the sun's surface (about 6000°C.), the hydrogen and helium that make up most of the sun's mass are unquestionably highly ionized and therefore constitute a plasma. MHD gives us considerable insight into the physically possible motions of hot solar plasma, but it is a young science and the turbulent sun has proven most recalcitrant. About all that can be said at present is that a sunspot pair is probably some relatively stable plasma structure—possibly like the vortex tube shown in the illustration. The rotating tube of conducting fluid is in effect an electromagnet and creates the strong sunspot magnetic field, or, just as possible, the field creates the vortex. Cause and effect are unresolved here. In one case, a periodic cause of mechanical turbulence must be found; in the other case, some eleven-year magnetic mechanism.

Apparently, the solar cornerstone of our model of solar-terrestrial relationships is not firmly in place, making the rest of the story somewhat suspect. Since the physical structure of a sunspot is not really known with confidence, it is hard to postulate a specific origin for the bridge that connects the sun and earth. The bridge has to come from someplace on the sun and wax and wane in step with the solar cycle. One tack to take is to be unspecific, which really means hiding the problem of specific cause behind a facade of generalities. Generalization begins with collecting a wide range of transient solar phenomena under the label *center of activity*, or CA. Typical features of a center of activity are the sunspots, prominences, flares,

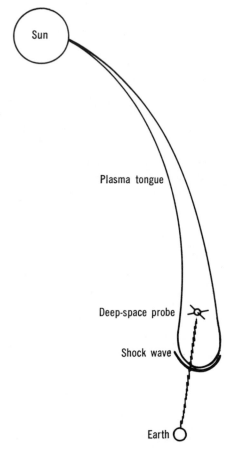

Sketch of a solar plasma tongue created by a center of activity on the solar surface. If the tongue envelops the earth, magnetic storms, auroras, and ionospheric disturbances are usually detected. A deep-space probe might radio an early warning of the tongue's approach.

faculae, and just about anything unusual. Because the sunspots are the most obvious features of a CA to a terrestrial observer, the activity of the entire sun—regardless of the specific type of activity —is measured by the sunspot number. The higher the sunspot count, the greater the solar activity, and the more pronounced the solar perturbations of earth. It is possible that sunspots may *not* be the direct cause of terrestrial activity but just a measure of some less obvious cause.

Before the days of satellites, the most apparent effects of solar activity upon the earth were the magnetic storms (seen in fluctuations of the compass needle), blackouts in long-distance radio communication, and lastly, the often breathtaking auroras that usually coincided with magnetic storms. Scientists quickly correlated the appearance of a flare on the surface of the sun with the disruption of long-distance radio communication a few seconds later. There was no doubt that short wavelength electromagnetic radiation from the flare was penetrating deep into the earth's atmosphere, causing the ionization of the air. Under ordinary conditions, the sun's radiation creates the well-known ionospheric layers at fifty miles altitude and above. These layers of free electrons and ions aid rather than hinder long-distance radio communication. Solar flare radiation, however, consists of shorter wavelengths and penetrates farther into the atmosphere (down to forty miles), so far that radio waves are absorbed as their energy is passed on to free electrons which quickly collide with the very dense surrounding molecules. Radio-waves are not reflected by this ionized layer. In addition, strong, temporary electrical currents are produced in the atmosphere when the pulse of flare radiation hits it. These currents are partially responsible for the transient magnetic fields that cause tremors in compass needles on the ground. If the magnetic flucuations are strong enough, electrical currents are induced in the long telephone wires crisscrossing the continents, and long-distance communication is further disrupted. When the sun is very active, long-distance earth communications are sometimes blacked out for days at a time. Cause and effect are easy to connect in the case of sudden ionospheric disturbances.

The main phases of magnetic storms do not begin until about *twenty hours* after visual sighting of obvious solar activity—usually a large flare. Dividing the distance from the sun by the travel time of the disturbance yields a velocity far lower than that of the electromagnetic radiation that causes sudden disturbances. The new stimulus must be some form of slow-moving particulate radiation, probably a cloud of plasma projected outward by the sun during a convulsion of its surface.

Before the satellites, the concept of tongues of solar plasma enveloping the earth was only a creature of inference. The closely connected idea of an electrical *ring current* of charged solar particles surrounding the earth where it is held captured by the earth's magnetic field was suggested by the Norwegian Carl Störmer as early as 1904, but he had no experimental proof. Adolph Schmidt, in Germany, proposed the magnetic capture of solar plasma in 1916 to explain the main phase of a magnetic storm. As early as this, without a shred of direct evidence, theorists identified the sun as a source of charged particles. In 1958, a young physicist at the University of Chicago, E. N. Parker, presented an analysis of the solar corona that suggested that there was a *continuous* efflux of plasma from the sun. This flow was over and above any clouds or tongues of plasma spewed out by solar CA's. Parker's steady plasma flow has now been dubbed the *solar wind*. It continually streams past the earth.

Direct measurements of steady and transient solar plasma were not made by the first earth satellites; their orbits were well below an unexpected structure now called the *magnetopause*. The first Explorer satellites did, however, discover the belts of *trapped radiation* that lie within the magnetopause. Only when deep space probes and satellites in highly eccentric orbits began to pierce the protective shell of the magnetopause did instruments begin to measure solar wind and plasma tongues that had been predicted. The experiments firmly established solar plasma as the carrier of solar influence. Measured velocities of hydrogen plasma confirmed Parker's estimates. Wind density proved to be about ten or twenty particles per cubic centimeter. Theorists, despite this victory, were startled by the complexity and geometry of the satellite-drawn interfaces that partially insulated the earth from the interplanetary "weather" and the weather maker, the sun.

During the first decade of the Space Age probes and satellites, carrying magnetometers and plasma detectors, sketched out a tear-shaped geomagnetic cavity with a long "tail" that stretches hundreds of thousands of miles away from the earth. The tail does not trail the earth as it moves around the sun, but rather it is "blown" by the solar wind in the direction *away from the sun.* Astronomers now believe that the solar wind also blows comet tails away from the sun.

The boundary of the geomagnetic cavity, the magnetopause, is really a shock front created as the fast-moving solar plasma collides

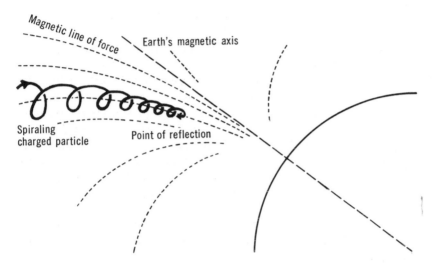

Schematic showing how charged particles in the radiation belts are reflected in the polar regions where the magnetic lines of force converge. Such magnetic "mirrors" trap the charged particles. If the particles collide with atoms in the polar atmosphere they will be removed from the radiation belts.

("interacts" is a better word) with the earth's magnetic field. It is the mutual interaction of the solar plasma and the earth's magnetic lines of force that produces the streamlined magnetosphere. The shock wave surrounding a cannonball in supersonic motion through air is similar in many respects; but the solar wind blows at 1500 miles per second and is so rarefied that the drag force exerted on earth satellites is minute, though measurable over many orbits.

Within the safe harbor of the magnetopause things are much quieter than out in the open interplanetary sea. Some of the more energetic charged particles in the solar wind are not turned away by the earth's field and leak through the magnetopause to be trapped in the radiation belts and perhaps channeled into the polar zones where they generate the auroras as they collide with atoms in the upper atmosphere causing them to radiate light.

The solar wind is not the only source of charged particles for the belts. Cosmic rays, which are much more energetic than the solar plasma particles, are not easily turned aside by the earth's field. Many readily penetrate the magnetosphere and are brought to a stop somewhere in the atmosphere or the solid earth. Cosmic rays colliding with air atoms in the high atmosphere cause nuclear reactions that produce neutrons, some of which pass through the radiation belts. The neutron is an unstable particle with a half life of only twelve minutes. Many neutrons are created as cosmic rays collide with the atmosphere and disintegrate into electrons, protons, and neutrinos in the region of the radiation belts. The electrons and protons are frequently captured by the magnetic field and help replenish the populations of the belts. The word "replenish" is appropriate because the electrons and protons trapped in the belts are also steadily lost as they collide with air molecules in the upper polar atmosphere.

Particles in the belts of trapped radiation thus come from two major sources: solar plasma that leaks in through the magnetopause and disintegrating neutrons created by collisions of cosmic rays with the atmosphere. The mapping of the radiation belts has been one of the most significant contributions of satellites to geophysics. The accepted picture of the belts shows electrons and protons spiraling about the earth's magnetic lines of force as they are reflected back and forth from pole to pole. Reflection of the charged particles occurs where the magnetic lines of force converge in the polar regions. Magnetic reflection of this sort is often employed in the laboratory to confine plasma in *magnetic bottles*. The deeper the trapped particles penetrate into the polar atmosphere, the more likely they are to hit an air molecule and be knocked out of the belt. As mentioned earlier, it is this interaction between the trapped particles and the atmosphere that is at least partially responsible for the auroras. This idea agrees nicely with the theoretical model showing solar plasma as the major cause of the auroras. Trapped particles that are not immediately removed from the belts in the polar regions are reflected back and forth until they are—something that may take several hundred years. Reflection from one pole to another takes only about a second. Superimposed on the rapid reflections from pole to pole is a steady drift of electrons and protons around the earth that creates a continuous shell of particles flashing

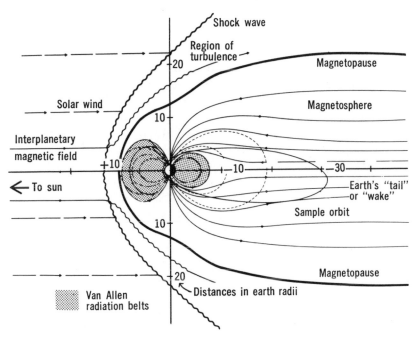

Current view of the magnetopause as it is shaped by the flow of solar plasma and action of the earth's magnetic field. The earth's "tail" probably extends even farther than the moon.

between the magnetic poles. Protons move from east to west and trapped electrons drift in the opposite direction.

The geometry and panorama presented by this picture of the magnetosphere and its contents have a certain grandeur, but many unresolved problems remain. The detail of the transfer of particles between the solar plasma, the trapped radiation belts, the earth's ionosphere, and the earth's upper atmosphere is far from well known. Particles "dumped" into the auroral regions certainly help generate some of the displays, but they apparently cannot account for all the features. The situation is similar to terrestrial meteorology where the major processes are well established but details are frustratingly elusive. As for the correlations that show solar influence on plant growth, the price of fox skins, and terrestrial weather, not to mention the stock market and other facets of human enterprise, there are no accepted cause-and-effect models that include them.

Summarizing, there are three major pieces to the model of the solar-terrestrial system. At the "cause" end of the cause-and-effect chain, cyclic solar activity is the demonstrated cause of much cyclic terrestrial activity; but the physical processes occurring on the sun that cause terrestrial ups and downs are not well understood. Neither is the clockwork mechanism that controls the eleven-year solar cycle. The second portion of the model, the bridge to earth, is in far better shape. The bridge transporting solar effects to earth consists of two parts: the short wavelength electromagnetic radiation that is responsible for sudden ionospheric disturbances and the jets of solar plasma ejected by the sun during its fits of activity. At the terrestrial end of the bridge, satellites and probes have sketched out the teardrop-shaped magnetosphere and drawn the routes taken by some of the charged particles from the time they penetrate the magnetopause until they are slowed to a stop in the atmosphere. The gross picture of sun-induced terrestrial activity seems sound, but the ever-elusive details, such as the explanation of all colors and innuendos of the auroras, have yet to be discovered.

There are more links to the cause-and-effect chain than meet the eye. After all, a complete story should begin with an explanation of why there is an eleven-year solar cycle instead of the mere statement that one exists. Possibly the sun has some naturally recurring internal disturbance that repeats every eleven years, just as Old Faithful erupts on schedule due to a natural build-up of steam pressure. It is also possible that an external cause of solar activity exists. Such a stimulus would have to be periodic in character to be convincing, but the only periodic phenomenon external to the sun and still close enough to have an effect is the motion of the solar-system planets. As the planets swing around the sun, their gravitational fields might conceivably stir the liquid surface of the sun into action in the same way that the moon creates tides in the seas and the rocky mantle of the earth. In particular, strong effects might be expected when the two biggest planets, Jupiter and Saturn, are lined up reinforcing one another. The thought is not a new one; it has been popping up in scientific journals since 1900.

"Shades of astrology," the perceptive reader will say. If the positions of the planets control the solar activity and solar activity has all sorts of consequences in earthly affairs, science is saying that the soothsayers have had something after all during the last two thousand years. Of course, the thought that the planets might be the cause of solar activity is only a *hypothesis,* one that may be refuted tomorrow. Next, although some scientists would be appalled if science supported astrology after centuries of bitter controversy and icy disdain, there would be many other scientists who would appreciate the irony. If there is some *small* truth to astrology, the thing to do is explain this truth in scientific terms and strip all the pretense away. There have been many instances, particularly in medicine, where science has reluctantly admitted that there has been some substance to old wives' tales and primitive remedies.

What does physics say about the possibility of the planets raising storms on the sun's surface? Offhand, the sun seems so much larger than the planets that their gravitational effects would seem to be too small. The mass of all the planets and asteroids put together only amounts to about 0.1% of the mass of the sun, and most of this is confined to Jupiter and Saturn. No one can doubt that the gravitational forces exerted by Jupiter and Saturn *can* cause tide-like effects in the highly fluid sun; the question really involves how such small forces can stimulate comparatively violent events such as sunspot groups a hundred thousand miles across. No physical mechanism has been proposed other than gravity-induced turbulence.

The most convincing argument of the proponents of planetary influence lies in the periodicity of the gravitational forces exerted on the sun. If all of the equations describing planetary motion about the sun are combined with those describing gravitational influence at the sun's surface, a strong cycle of 11.08 years duration is found. R. M. Wood and K. D. Wood, who reported these results in the October 9, 1965, issue of the British journal *Nature,* also state that planetary influence may also explain the alternation of sunspot magnetic polarity, the commencement of new sunspot cycles at the same solar latitude, and the other cycles that have been found in sunspot statistics. The last item refers to the fact that sunspot cycles only *average* eleven years and may vary from seven years to sixteen years. This variability may be explained by supposing that there are other cyclic effects superimposed on the basic eleven-year cycle that hurry or delay the sunspot peaks. The Woods also show that the inner planets (Mercury through Mars) are important in determining the gravitational forces impressed upon the sun. Although the masses of the inner planets are considerably smaller than that of Jupiter, they are much closer to the sun.

The only way to support this hypothesis (or model) that claims to account for solar activity is with pencil, paper, and computer. Experiments with planets and gravity are not within our power— at least not yet! The English scientist D. G. King-Hele, by way of illustration, has predicted the dates and intensities of the next two sunspot maxima based on the combined gravitational influence of the planets. "Theoretical experiments" such as this may eventually convince a skeptical scientific community, or, conversely, some computation may pull all support out from under the hypothesis. If King-Hele's predictions are borne out in fact, a few more people will line up behind the hypothesis.

The less controversial sun-earth cause-and-effect chains are now being explored with spacecraft. The sun, being a star like those discussed in the preceding chapter, emits much of its energy in the X-ray and ultraviolet regions of the spectrum. These rays are blocked by our atmosphere, making satellites and deep-space probes valuable instrument carriers for solar physicists. Several Orbiting Solar Observatories, called OSOs, have already been launched. Ultraviolet and X-ray instruments on these satellites repeatedly scan the sun's disk in a zigzag "roster," or pattern, to sketch out the sun's image (including the centers of activity) in light that never reaches the earth's surface. Between the sun and earth, deep space probes, such as Mariner 4 and Pioneer 6, radio back measurements of the solar plasma flux and the asociated magnetic fields. At the earth end, instrument carriers such as the Orbiting Geophysical Observatory (OGO) pass directly through the radiation belts, the auroras, and magnetopause. Sounding rockets are also shot up into the ionosphere and auroral regions to make *in situ* measurements. The substantiation or refutation of the details of the sun-earth model sketched in this chapter depend upon the long-term collection and correlation of data all the way from sun to earth. To illustrate: a watching OSO might signal the beginning of a solar flare: a few hours later, Pioneer 6 and other probes out in deep space, might catch the leading edge of the plasma tongue on its instruments and radio the data to earth. Still later, if the plasma tongue engulfs the earth, satellites will follow the plasma particles as they penetrate into the magnetosphere and spiral down along the earth's magnetic lines of force and cause auroras.

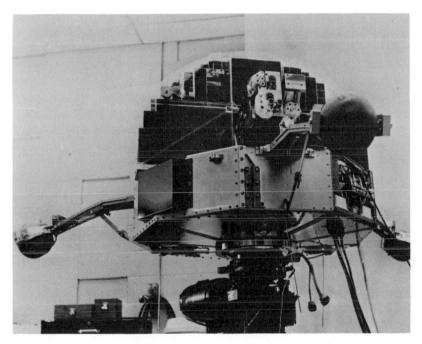

Photograph of an Orbiting Solar Observatory (OSO). Instruments mounted on the "sail" sweep back and forth across the sun's face recording its structure at wavelengths that never reach terrestrial astronomers. Nine-sided base is 112 cm across.

READING LIST

ELLISON, M. A. *The Sun and Its Influence*, Routledge and Kegan Paul, Ltd., London, 1959.
All the books listed at the end of Chapter 5.

7

JUPITER'S WANDERING RED SPOT AND OTHER IDIOSYNCRASIES

A space probe launched outward away from the sun will intersect the orbit of Mars at about 140,000,000 miles from the sun. Mars is the last outpost of the inner "terrestrial" group of planets. Beyond lies a planetless gap of nearly 340,000,000 miles that is swept at intervals by swarms of asteroids, planetoids, and other rocky debris. If the space probe survives its passage across this gap and if its timing is right, it will rendezvous with a gigantic flattened spheroid of gases, ices, and heaven knows what peculiar states of matter. This is Jupiter; colossus of solar system planets; the true "planet of mystery;" and the first of the outer non-terrestrial planets.

A successful Jupiter probe would radio back new facts about the planet across hundreds of millions of intervening miles to the huge, earlike antennas waiting on earth. But, if history is borne out, each new fact about Jupiter will only deepen the mystery surrounding this banded giant that could swallow the earth 1300 times over.

Jupiter is an alien planet and little of our terrestrial experience seems of much use in understanding it. The planet is brilliant in the night sky and has been known from antiquity. Even some of its earth-sized moons are visible to the naked eye on occasion. The first telescopes and spectroscopes scanned its face hundreds of years ago; but today we still seem far from a viable model for Jupiter. Not that there are not models; there are too many. Every year brings new ones. Eventually, some models will disintegrate under the impact of new facts, while one or two others will be strengthened. And once the key to Jupiter is discovered, models for the other major planets (Saturn, Uranus, and Neptune) should also follow. Because Jupiter possesses more than two thirds of all the mass circling the sun, understanding this planet probably means understanding the origin of the solar system itself.

One model of Jupiter builds the planet from the same basic stuff as the sun; hydrogen and helium. Jupiter in this view is a tiny star that never became luminous because the energy of gravitational contraction never heated it to temperatures at which thermonuclear reactions could become self-sustaining. As if to emphasize its similarity to the sun, Jupiter has spots that wax and wane, including one, the Great Red Spot, that astronomers have puzzled over for hundreds of years. Jupiter also boasts "activity" of various sorts with peculiar cyclic features. Unlike the sun's cyclic eruptions of plasma and short wavelength radiation, Jupiter emits radio waves that seem to be correlated with the positions of several of its large, close satellites. There are also startling color changes. However, the purpose of this chapter is not to prove that Jupiter emulates the sun, though the parallels are fascinating, but to describe how models of Jupiter have evolved, with emphasis on the roles played by the Great Red Spot and the recently discovered radio emissions.

Observers seeing Jupiter through the telescope for the first time often seem to sense immediately and intuitively its hugeness and alien character. The planet is almost grotesquely squashed at its poles by centrifugal force, being 88,700 miles in diameter at the equator and only 82,800 miles from pole to pole. The yellowish, reddish, bluish, sometimes brownish bands vividly split Jupiter into zones that early astronomers quickly associated with our earthly climatic zones. Frequently Jupiter's large inner moons sweep across its face, casting eerie, near-circular shadows below on the planetary disk. Quite understandably, Jupiter was first cast as an earthlike planet; huge, to be sure, and clouded, too, but probably sustaining God's children beneath the bands of clouds.

More thorough study of Jupiter's features quickly undermines any illusions about earthly properties. After a half hour of watching, Jupiter has rotated perceptibly. It turns on its axis in only 9 hours and 55 minutes, faster than any other solar system planet. The cloud belts rotate at different speeds. The colors of the clouds change, and various short-lived spots and other "disturbances" come and go. Visual observations of color and structure show the strangeness of Jupiter, but it is the physical measurements that make us realize how alien the planet really is. Studies of the Red Spot and radio emissions underscore this strangeness. However, the fact that Jupiter is radically different from earth doesn't make it a maverick or outcast; it may be the typical planet type gracing other stellar systems. Astronomers have already detected large, non-luminous bodies in orbit around nearby stars through their gravitational effects on the visible companion. Earth and the other terrestrial planets may be the real oddballs in the skies.

Gravitational effects also led to the first accurate mass determination for Jupiter. The talented accountant-turned-astronomer, Friedrich Wilhelm Bessel, discovered this planet's unearthly conformation and contents. Bessel's research employed lengthy, exceedingly complex computations involving the orbital periods of Jupiter's large inner moons, the degree of planetary flattening, and other factors. Bessel published the results of his labors (which today would be done by computers) in *Astronomische Untersuchungen,* in 1842. He found that Jupiter's mass was roughly 388 times that of the earth (now measured as 318 times that of earth). The surprise came in comparing this result with Jupiter's volume, which was believed to be about 1318 times that of the earth. Apparently, the mean density of Jupiter was only 1.33 times that of water and less than one-fourth that of earth.

All thoughts of a terrestrial Jupiter vanished. The idea of a substantial, hard-surface planet dissolved in the swirling gases and seething liquids that now seemed Jupiter's substance.

As Willy Ley writes in *Watchers of the Skies:* "All the facts suggested just one thing: heat." In 1874, Hermann Carl Vogel, a German pioneer in spectroscopic astronomy, reinforced this thought when he found that although Jupiter's spectrum was primarily that of reflected sunlight there seemed to be self-luminosity at the red end of the spectrum. The American astronomer Henry Draper found additional observational evidence in 1880. This was apparently enough for those who popularized science in those days. In his *Other Worlds Than Ours*, published in 1896, Professor Richard A. Proctor leapt to a hot, bubbling, red-glowing model of Jupiter. This was the only way, Proctor claimed, the "vitality" of Jupiter could be explained. This "cauldron" model of Jupiter was consistent with observations of the times, but stranger models were yet to come as more physical measurements were made. The cauldron model as least achieved Proctor's main objective, which was the scientific coup de grâce for the then widely held notion that Jupiter and the other planets were inhabited.

A logical way to evaluate the concept of a hot Jupiter was to compute the energy sources available that might be responsible for the planet's vitality. Energy input from the sun is completely inadequate at 485 million miles; and most of the heat left over from gravitational condensation during the planet's birth should either have been radiated away or confined below a thick, insulating layer of solid rock (as it is on earth). Neither of these energy sources seemed to support the hot Jupiter that Proctor promulgated. In the 1920s Harold Jeffreys, the English astronomer, computed the only other source of energy left to a body too small to support thermonuclear reactions: radioactivity. Jeffreys' calculations showed that the amount of radioactivity required to generate appreciable heat on Jupiter would have to be many thousand times that measured in the earth's crust. This seemed out of the question—if the planets all had a common origin. Jupiter, in the light of these findings, *must* be cold rather than hot.

Jeffreys was even more specific. He suggested that Jupiter had a small solid core wrapped up in a thick ice layer, which, in turn, was surrounded by a deep atmosphere of hydrogen, helium, nitrogen, oxygen, and possibly methane. The swiftly rotating clouds might be frozen crystals of carbon dioxide. About the same time, 1926, Donald H. Menzel and his associates at Harvard concluded from infrared measurements of Jupiter with a radiometer (quite different from Vogel's spectrometer) that the planet's temperature was about $-226°F$; certainly cold enough to support Jeffreys' refrigerator model. In three decades the model of Jupiter went from one temperature extreme to the other.

A few notes of caution must be interjected here. First, nothing has been said yet about the Great Red Spot and the radio emissions from Jupiter. Then there are the 1874 observations by Vogel indicating infrared emission by Jupiter. Those old spectroscopic measurements were widely interpreted at the time as being due to thermal radiation from a hot planet. What Vogel actually had recorded in 1874 was the presence of a dark band of spectral absorption lines that were missing in the solar spectrum. It was an out-

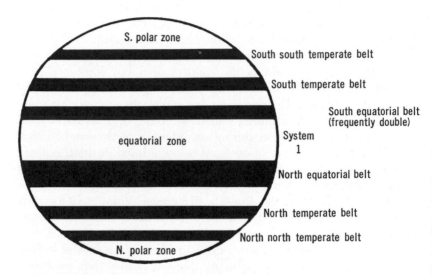

The cloud belts of Jupiter. The Great Red Spot, when visible, is located in the South Temperate Belt. The north pole is shown at the bottom of the page, as it appears in the telescope.

right misinterpretation of one of these bands that led to the early conclusion that Jupiter was hot. Still more dark bands and lines were found subsequently. Something in the atmosphere of Jupiter was definitely absorbing part of the incident sunlight before it was reflected back toward earth. The only trouble was that no one could identify the chemical compounds doing the absorbing; there were no laboratory absorption spectra like them.

In 1931 the German-born astronomer Rupert Wildt suggested that these mysterious absorption lines might be due to methane and ammonia on Jupiter's upper atmosphere. To confirm or demolish Wildt's hypothesis, Theodore Dunham at the Mount Wilson Observatory compressed methane and ammonia gases in a sixty-foot pipe. By sending light back and forth through the gases with mirrors, he found that methane and ammonia did absorb light at wavelengths identical to the dark lines in Jupiter's spectrum. Methane and ammonia were surely present in the upper atmosphere, but scientists believed that they were only minor constituents. But science popularization went astray and the general public was told that Jupiter and the other major planets had rather disagreeable atmospheres "mainly" of methane and ammonia. Further research showed this inference to be erroneous, but many books were printed incorporating this misconception.

Two other experiments have been employed to plumb the atmosphere of Jupiter. The first made use of the fact that Jupiter passed in front of (occulted) the star Sigma Arietis on the night of November 20, 1952. By carefully measuring the change in the star's light intensity as the atmosphere of Jupiter gradually blotted it out, the American astronomers W. A. Baum and A. D. Code, using a spectroscope on the Mount Wilson sixty-inch telescope, were able to show that the mean molecular weight of the gases in Jupiter's upper atmosphere was between three and four. Methane and ammonia, with molecular weights of sixteen and seventeen, respectively could not be very important components of the *upper* atmosphere by this evidence. Hydrogen and helium were much more likely.

The next significant observation was made in 1960 when C. C. Kiess, C. H. Corliss, and H. K. Kiess at the U.S. Bureau of Standards finally measured the emission lines of molecular hydrogen, confirming what had been supposed from the low molecular weight. If it seems strange that hydrogen was not detected earlier by spectroscopists, it should be recalled that low temperatures excite few emission lines.

Today evidence seems to favor an atmosphere dominated by hydrogen and helium; with methane, ammonia, and other heavy gases present as impurities. The relative amounts of hydrogen and helium are the subject of considerable controversy. Some investigators favor an atmosphere composed of as much as 97% helium; others lean toward hydrogen as the major constituent. Observations are not precise enough to be sure. One thing is certain, however— the experimental data are superficial in the sense that they come from only the outer layers of Jupiter's atmosphere. The only clues we have to Jupiter's interior is the average planet density (1.33 times that of water), the shape of its gravitational field as revealed by the motion of its moons, and what is revealed by cloud motions and color changes.

The model of Jupiter that convinces the most people today is not universally welcomed; nor can we believe that this model will prove to be permanent. However, it provides a convenient foundation for the forthcoming discussion of the Great Red Spot and Jupiter's sporadic radio emissions.

For the moment we have the following picture drawn by W. C. DeMarcus in the United States, W. H. Ramsey in England, and V. G. Fesenkov and A. G. Massevich in Russia. First, the model states that on Jupiter there are about fourteen atoms of hydrogen for every one of helium, plus a minor amount of impurities. Most of the helium is in the planet's center, which turns out to be a most singular structure. Modern pressure-density-temperature equations describing the behavior of matter suggest that at a distance of about one-fifth of the way from cloud tops to planet center, the pressure has risen to a fantastic two million atmospheres, or about 30,000,000 pounds per square inch. At this pressure, the molecular hydrogen turns into a solid with many of the properties of a metal, such as high electrical conductivity. "Metallic" hydrogen persists to the planet's center where it is compressed by pressures approaching 100 million atmospheres to a density of possibly thirty times that of water (heavier than any element under normal conditions). The temperature at Jupiter's center is postulated to be a few thousand degrees, while the outer regions of the atmosphere are very cold, just as experiment requires. Jupiter, then, would seem to be constructed of the same basic stuff as the sun and other stars, only it is too cold and too small to turn itself into a self-sustaining thermonuclear furnace. Jupiter almost seems to be a star that didn't make the grade.

Often the foundation of a house is not nearly as intriguing as the shutters, the gables, or some eye-catching decoration. As astronomical mysteries go, the Great Red Spot of Jupiter undeniably ranks with the canals of Mars and the sunspots. Though the Red Spot seems only a superficial aspect of a planet that dwarfs every other object in the solar system save the sun, perhaps the Red Spot is symptomatic of deeper phenomena. Just as sunspots help diagnose the sun, so may the Great Red Spot tell us hidden things about Jupiter.

When the Great Red Spot of Jupiter is brick red with activity, no observer, even with a small telescope, can miss it. It is hard to overlook an area 30,000 miles long and 10,000 miles wide (roughly

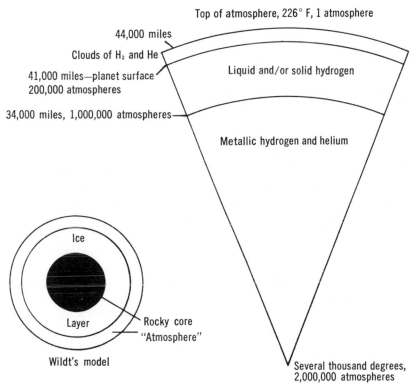

Wildt's early model of Jupiter contrasted with the most popular modern model.

four times the earth's cross section), particularly when color and shape set it apart from the cloud bands. Much of the time, though, the Red Spot is pale and almost invisible, without vivid contrast. During these periods, it seems just a "hollow" or outline in Jupiter's south temperate zone. Still, its general shape and size remain despite its temporary reticence.

Robert Hooke, the persistent baiter of Isaac Newton, was probably the first to record the Red Spot. In 1664 he drew Jupiter show-ing a dark spot in its southern hemisphere that most likely was the famed Spot. Drawings of the Italian-French astronomer Giovanni Cassini, made in 1672 and 1691, record the Red Spot for certain. The Spot really attracted attention when it flared up in 1878. Wilhelm Tempel drew many astronomers' telescopes to the now-conspicuous object with his 1879 paper in *Astronomische Nach-richten.* For four years it was *the* great mystery in astronomy and the subject of much discussion. Then, unaccountably it faded and so did interest. According to the thinking of 1878, Jupiter was an earthlike planet, and the sudden appearance (Hooke's and Cassini's prior observations were not connected with the Red Spot at that time) and subsequent fading pointed toward a terrestrial phenom-enon such as a colossal volcano or lava flow that threw red reflec-tions on the clouds hurrying overhead. A few more imaginative thinkers supposed that a planetoid had perhaps crashed into Jupiter, or, even more stimulating and cataclysmic, that Jupiter was prepar-ing to give birth to another moon and would soon throw off a vast mass of molten planet stuff.

Once the excitement surrounding the heightened visibility of the Spot during the 1878–1882 period died down, astronomers went back to their journals and found that the Great Red Spot had a long but not well-publicized history. The name of Heinrich Schwabe again came to the fore. He was the German amateur astronomer who had recorded sunspot patterns with incredible diligence for seventeen years in the early nineteenth century. Schwabe apparently was also intrigued with spots elsewhere for he drew and reported the Great Red Spot in 1831. No one took much notice.

Since the Spot seemed to be part of Jupiter's permanent cast of mysteries, the thoughts of planetoid splashdowns and moon births quickly disappeared. Next, a few astronomers sat back to watch the Spot more carefully as it faded to a light pink in 1882.

In a little over a decade, the Spot flared into brilliance again. Summarizing this sporadic aspect, the Spot has been most brilliant during the following periods: 1878–1882, 1893–1894, 1903–1907, 1911, 1914, 1919–1920, 1926–1927, 1936–1937, 1957–1958, and 1961. What-ever model is constructed to explain the Spot, it must have an in-ternally or externally stimulated mechanism for turning the planet brick red over an area of some 300 million square miles.

To confound the model makers, not only does the size of the Spot vary; it wanders like a gypsy over several degrees of latitude. It also rotates at rates different from the surrounding cloud bands. The British amateur astronomer Bertrand Peek has assiduously kept detailed records of the Spot's position and appearance over the years. Peek is now the foremost authority on Jupiter, and his book *The Planet Jupiter* is the classic work on this strange planet. Peek's records of drifting coordinates seem proof positive that the Red Spot cannot be anchored to Jupiter's solid surface if it has one, but instead "floats" erratically in the atmosphere. But one can never be sure about Jupiter.

With only the clues of variable color, shape, and position to guide theorists, it was natural to think of the Spot as some monstrous "iceberg" suspended in Jupiter's dense atmosphere. Obviously, ordinary water ice would be out of keeping with the current view that Jupiter is largely hydrogen and helium. Peek has suggested a floe of helium ice that rises and falls as the density of the surrounding fluid varies. The iceberg floats high in the liquid or dense atmosphere when the Spot is prominent and low when it is not. This is a rather bizarre thought—several earth's worth of solid helium drifting amidst fast-moving bands of colored clouds of thousands of miles in width. From what we know, however, Jupiter is bizarre enough without the Red Spot.

If the thought of a cryogenic iceberg is too unsettling, look for more facts. Short-lived spots are common on both Jupiter and Saturn. Do they provide any clues to the nature of the larger and more permanent Red Spot? Most of the spots last only a few days and are of little help. A fascinating exception is the great eruption that is now dignified as the South Tropical Disturbance. On February 28, 1901, the astronomer P. B. Molesworth picked out a dark hump at the edge of the South Equatorial Current (one of Jupiter's bands). The hump quickly became a spot that spread across the belt and elongated. Like the Red Spot, it rotated around the planet at a different rate than the surrounding clouds. In fact, it moved faster than the Great Red Spot which was cruising along nearby at a more southerly latitude. Every two or three years the South Tropical Disturbance caught up with and passed the Great Red Spot. As these immense apparitions came abreast, there was decided interaction, much as two passing bars of soap affect one another in the bathtub. The Disturbance seemed to drag the Spot along with it for several thousand miles, only to release it and permit it to float back to its original position. The visual observations had strong hydrodynamic or "fluid" overtones. Unfortunately, the South Tropical Disturbance with all its potential diagnostic value has not been seen since 1941.

Following this hydrodynamic hint, R. Hide of MIT has recently proposed a somewhat different model for the Red Spot, one that also is consistent with observations and the best models of the planet-as-a-whole. Hide has shown that winds rushing over a large discontinuity on Jupiter's solid surface, such as a shallow depression or plateau with the Spot's linear dimensions, would create a vertical convection column that would reach upward through the thick cloud cover to the upper reaches of the atmosphere where it would be visible to us as the Great Red Spot. A terrestrial analogy would be the relatively stationary clouds formed when winds flow over mountain ranges; viz., the Sierra Wave. To account for the Spot's motion, a floating surface feature would also be plausible. If the gaseous column rising from the discontinuity is a long one it might twist and weave like a tornado, giving apparent motion to a stationary stimulus. Many have thought that the Spot might be a tornado-like vortex in Jupiter's atmosphere. The oval shape of the Spot and the fact that ends of the oval are sometimes pointed have discouraged such presumptions. The mechanism proposed by Hide depends upon what is called a *Taylor column* in hydrodynamics. The hydrodynamic model accounts for the relative permanence of the Red Spot and still permits some variability in form, position, and visibility. Generally speaking, the hydrodynamic model is similar to Peek's iceberg model, except that Peek lets us see the disturbing object while Hide shows us only the disturbance the object creates in the atmosphere.

More recently Carl Sagan, an American astronomer, has added a corollary to Hide's model that permits even more superficial variation. Sagan supposes that the red color of the Spot arises from the excitation of organic molecules at the top of the Taylor column by electrical discharges or perhaps solar radiation and plasma. Changes in color and visibility could then come from variations in the excitation source.

In sum, the explanations or models of the Great Red Spot have fluctuated as violently as the planetary models of Jupiter. Each new fact of significance has given birth to a new model. And naturally, like the tail on the dog, the model of the Spot has to wag in step with the model of the planet. For the moment, both models are cryogenic in character and are thousands of degrees away in temperature from red hot lava flows and seething cauldrons of yore.

Just when nature seems intransigent and science has apparently worn out its best experimental tools, somebody uncovers a new technique that adds new dimensions to sticky problems, permitting us to see phenomena from a new vantage point. The preceding chapters have illustrated how powerful a tool radio astronomy has been in cosmology and solar physics. Despite this productive history it comes as something of a surprise when radio astronomy helps us unravel the shroud of mystery enveloping an ice-cold planet like Jupiter. What physical processes transpire in ices and gases near absolute zero that could possibly generate radio waves?

Radio waves from Jupiter were undoubtedly recorded many times by radio astronomers before they were recognized as being of planetary origin. After all, frigid Jupiter *should not* emit radio waves and therefore no one looked; and if Jupiter crossed the antenna pattern of a radio telescope and its emissions happened to be recorded, the data were rejected or ignored.

Jupiter was first recognized as a radio emitter in early 1955 when B. F. Burke and F. L. Franklin, working at the Carnegie Institute at Seneca, Maryland, associated strong periodic bursts of radio noise at wavelengths of 13.5 meters with that planet. Radio astronomers immediately searched their old records (not really so old in youthful radio astronomy) for recorded signals that might have originated on Jupiter.

In Australia, a country extremely strong in radio astronomy, C. A. Shain found data from 1950 and 1951 that most definitely came from Jupiter. The signals had originally been written off as due to terrestrial thunderstorms. Shain's records were good enough to permit him to estimate the period of the noise emissions: They waxed and waned every nine hours and fifty-five minutes; in synchronism with some of the rotating cloud bands on Jupiter. A radio noise maker was apparently being swept around the planet with the cloud systems.

After the unexpected find of Burke and Franklin, many radio

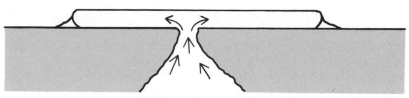

Red-hot lava flow model

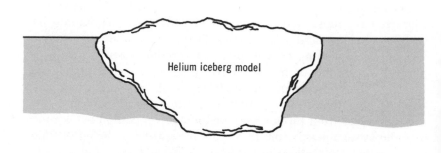

Helium iceberg model

Red spot, perhaps stimulated by solar radiation   Top of atmosphere

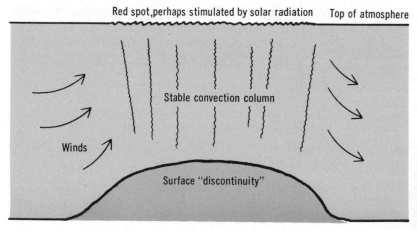

Stable convection column

Winds

Surface "discontinuity"

Some Red Spot models.

telescopes zeroed in on Jupiter whenever it appeared above the horizon. Radiowise the planet became as complex and singular as it is when seen by visible light. Radio waves have been picked up with wavelengths in the centimeter range, in the decimeter range (tens of centimeters), and in the decameter range (tens of meters). Radiation in each range requires a different explanation. But this is an advantage; the more *different* data the better when dealing with a planet as unpredictable as Jupiter.

Starting at the short wavelength end of the observed radio spectrum, the centimeter radio noise has an obvious explanation: temperature. In retrospect, centimeter radiation should have been looked for earlier. The American radio astronomer C. H. Mayer and his associates first detected 3.15-cm radio noise from Jupiter in 1956. The strength of the signals turned out to be just about what one would expect from a planet the size of Jupiter with an atmospheric temperature of a hundred or so degrees below zero Fahrenheit. The centimeter waves seem definitely of thermal origin and are consistent with radiometric measurements of Jupiter's temperature. Cold though the planet's atmosphere might be, the free electrons vibrate fast enough to generate centimeter waves (10,000,000,000 times a second for 3-cm radio waves). Even ice generates "thermal" radiation.

In the decimeter range, measurements were not so reassuring. At a wavelength of 22 cm, the radio brightness of Jupiter inferred a temperature of over 5000°F. At 68 cm, the *apparent* temperature had risen to almost 130,000°F. Clearly, explanation in terms of thermal radiation would be ridiculous. The situation was similar to that in the sun's corona where radio temperatures of millions of degrees are measured. Some *non-thermal* physical process in the Jovian atmosphere was accelerating electrons and making them radiate in the decimeter region.

In 1959 G. B. Field made a suggestion in the *Journal of Geophysical Research* that seemed to explain all the known characteristics of Jupiter's decimeter radio waves. Field postulated that Jupiter possessed a strong magnetic field—possibly stronger than 1000 gauss—and that electrons were trapped by this field in the same way that they are in the earth's Van Allen belts. As the electrons spiral around the magnetic lines of force they are accelerated in the sense that they are pushed off a straight-line course. The accelerated electrons radiate radio waves just as electrons in a cyclotron or synchrotron atom smasher do. Similar radio waves have since been identified as coming from the earth's own belt of trapped radiation.

Further studies of Jupiter's decimeter radiation have shown that it seems to originate from a source much larger than the visible disk of the planet, as one would expect if it originated in thick trapped radiation belts surrounding it. At least some of the decimeter radiation can be correlated with solar activity in the same way that the earth's auroras and magnetic storms are associated with the sun. Tongues of solar plasma seem to reach out as far as Jupiter and "dump" charged particles into its magnetic bottle.

As satisfying as the radiation-belt hypothesis may be, theorists are hard put to explain the origin of a Jovian magnetic field two thousand times stronger than the earth's. If the source of the earth's field were known, the task might be easier. One theory of the earth's field depends upon dynamo action of circulating electric currents beneath the crust. Jupiter's field, to be susceptible to a similar explanation, would infer the presence of electrically conducting material somewhere under the obscuring cloud belts. Thus, the discovery of Jupiter's radio emissions has vital consequences for the modeling of the planet as a whole. The modern cryogenic model of Jupiter has a core of solid, metallic hydrogen and helium. This weird substance should be a good conductor of electricity and, combined with Jupiter's rapid rotation about its axis, may account for the formidable magnetic field required to explain the decimeter radio emissions. It is satisfying to see sun-Jupiter effects that parallel sun-earth effects. Such associations help knit the solar system together.

In a sense, it is somewhat ironical how solar activity affects Jupiter's decimeter emissions and how, in turn, Jupiter (stretching the imagination) may stimulate solar activity through its gravitational field. Who knows how many subtle ties there are between the sun and its planets?

Jupiter's decameter radiation, the third radio component, does not dovetail so neatly into our models. First to be discovered, it seems to be the last to yield to explanation. The decameter radiation is of the *noise-storm* type; it is not continuous, but occurs in bursts which have complex spectra. It is easy to understand how Shain believed it to be terrestrial thunderstorm activity because in actuality it may be due to lightning discharges in the atmosphere of Jupiter. The bursts are intense and well focused, lasting a few seconds each. A train of decameter noise bursts may radiate as much as 10,000 megawatts of power, an observation that fits well with the idea of electrical discharges in a turbulent atmosphere. An isolated noise burst tells little, but collectively they may release a clue.

These days astronomers are much more attuned to cyclic effects in celestial phenomena. Whenever solar system observations show a trace of a pattern in time, they first try to correlate them with the sun spot cycle. Jupiter's decameter radio-noise bursts seem to occur periodically so it was natural to check their appearance against sunspots. While some of Jupiter's color changes do seem to be sun-induced, correlation only showed that the decameter radiation was *inversely* associated with sunspots; that is, the more sunspots the less decameter noise. Countering this was the observation that decameter noise storms often occurred a few days following solar eruptions. The two pieces did not fit together in the puzzle. An entirely different and rather rash kind of correlation was reported by E. K. Bigg in *Nature* in 1964. Bigg maintained that Jupiter's decameter radio bursts were associated with the position of Jupiter's third largest satellite, Io. More thorough analysis of radio noise records over the span 1957–1965 have confirmed this correlation and have also indicated that the positions of the moons Europa and Ganymede influence the timing of the decameter emissions. Io has the strongest influence on the emissions; it is also the *closest, large* satellite of Jupiter.

Io is about 2000 miles in diameter and has an orbital radius of only 262,000 miles. Jupiter's visible diameter is 86,000 miles, putting Io close to the visible atmosphere and perhaps within the postulated magnetopause itself. If Io has a magnetic field of its own, magnetic stimulation of Jupiter's ionosphere and/or radiation belts might be suspected. Or, there may be tide-like gravitational interactions with the fluids (gases and liquids) surrounding the solid core. At the present time, the discovery of the effects of Io are so new that no detailed explanations have been worked out.

The thought of gravitational stimulation of radio-noise storms is most intriguing because of the similar connection proposed between

Jupiter and solar activity. Completing the analogy (which may prove to be completely erroneous and even ridiculous), Io and Jupiter, respectively, gravitationally interact with Jupiter and the sun, respectively, to cause electromagnetic activity that we can detect on the earth.

Where does the experimentalist turn next to ferret out the data on Jupiter? The very recent discovery of the effects of Io bears witness that plenty of work remains in the radio frequency region of the spectrum. The Radio Astronomy Explorer (RAE) satellite, launched in 1967, will open up that part of the radio spectrum below 15 Mc which has hithertofore been blocked by the earth's ionosphere. The RAE with its 750-foot antennas oriented toward Jupiter should give us more information about the decameter radiation. At the short wavelength of the electromagnetic spectrum—the ultraviolet and X-ray regions—where NASA's Orbiting Astronomical Observatory (OAO) can be of help, one expects to find little in the way of interest when short-wavelength instruments are directed toward Jupiter. Jupiter, however, is famous for its surprises; at least a look with the OAO seems the wise course.

As for the idea of the space probe fired directly at Jupiter, the astronautical literature brims with ideas for experiments and space vehicles to carry them. In view of the almost two years of time needed for the probe to reach Jupiter, the spacecraft and its instruments will have to be extremely reliable. The intense cold and reduced effectiveness of solar power supplies as the space probe recedes from the sun add to the mission's difficulties. Still, the unraveling of the mysteries of Jupiter has so much significance in the understanding of the entire solar system that Jupiter missions must follow on the heels of the current Mariner and Voyager probes to Mars and Venus.

Several experiments are clamoring for a vehicle that can transport them close to Jupiter:

The first Jupiter probe should carry a magnetometer to measure the magnetic field inferred from measurements of decimeter radio noise.

A microwave radiometer might be carried along to check earth-based measurements and, if possible, measure the planet's surface temperature at wavelengths that penetrate the atmosphere.

Charged-particle counters to measure the particles trapped in Jupiter's postulated radiation belts.

A TV camera to provide close-up photographs of Jupiter, after the fashion of Mariner 4 that gave us our first good glimpses of the Martian surface.

Several spectrometers to scan the planet's surface to give us detailed spectra of the cloud bands and the Red Spot at various wavelengths. Possibly, Jovian auroras might be detected with such an instrument.

This is the kind of road that astronomers would like to follow but Jupiter, ever unpredictable, may blossom forth with a new Great Red Spot tomorrow or begin bombarding us with X-rays or radiations equally unexpected. As Professor Proctor proclaimed in 1896 (but with an entirely different planetary model in mind), "Within the orb which presents so glorious an aspect upon our skies, processes of disturbance must be at work wholly different from any taking place on our own earth."

READING LIST

DULK, G. A. Io-Related Radio Emission from Jupiter, *Science, 148, 1585,* June 18, 1965.

GLASSTONE, S. *Sourcebook on the Space Sciences,* D. Van Nostrand Company, Princeton, 1965.

LEY, W. *Watchers of the Skies,* The Viking Press, New York, 1963.

MOORE, P. *The Planets,* W. W. Norton & Company, New York, 1962.

PEEBLES, P. J. E. The Big Planets, *International Science and Technology,* 32, Nov. 1964.

PEEK, B. M. *The Planet Jupiter,* The Macmillan Company, New York, 1958.

WHIPPLE, F. L. *Earth, Moon, and Planets,* Harvard University Press, Cambridge, 1963.

8

THE CANAL QUESTION

The chapter title evokes thoughts of a single planet: Mars. The canals of Mars and, more specifically, interpretations of them, raise the blood pressure of many an astronomer. The canals of Mars have caused as much excitement and bitter controversy as if Mars had been found to be a perfect cube or tetrahedron sailing around the sun. These thin, ephemeral wisps of lines have not even been seen by some of the world's best observers with topnotch telescopes at their disposal. Yet, for others, sometimes the earth's atmosphere holds still for an instant and through the telescope's eyepiece comes a crystal-clear vision of a network of fine lines incised in the Martian surface. Only the keenest eyes can catch these patterns and transcribe them onto maps.

Martian canals are like flying saucers in the sense that not everyone is privileged to see them, although almost everyone admits that there is some substance to the sightings. Controversy surges up when someone attributes either phenomenon to the work of intelligent beings. Strange, isn't it, that the same scientists who espouse curved space, the Big-Bang Theory, and other constructs so foreign to human experience, cannot bring themselves to consider *other life* as a reasonable hypothesis? Some, though certainly not all, scientists seem just as reluctant to see the earth displaced as the focal point of life as the critics of Copernicus were to hear the earth denied as the hub of the universe. The history of the Martian canals and the guesses about what they might be is as fascinating as any story in astronomy. When the curious psychologies of the *life* and *non-life* factions are added to the tale, it becomes irresistible.

First, though, what is needed to see the fabled canals? The requirements are a good telescope, a good site, and a good eye. It is tempting to add—a good imagination. Some of the canal watchers have been a little free with the pen in rendering what they saw (or believed they saw). They are counterbalanced by those who are sure there is nothing to see and, because of it, see nothing.

The human eye is a remarkable optical instrument attached to a computer par excellence—the brain. In stellar astronomy, photographic film and photometers supplant the eye at the telescope because the eye and brain cannot cope with the thousands of images of varying intensities on the average star plate. But for planetary astronomy, the eye-brain combination is unbeatable. On clear nights, far from city lights, planetary astronomers swing their telescopes to the planets and—if they are lucky—they will see, not the fuzzy, smudgy images that film records, but multicolored spheres floating tantalizingly in space, covered with vague markings. On the best nights, there may be brief instants when our atmosphere stops quivering altogether and the observer sees more detail on a planet's surface than he has during a lifetime at the telescope eyepiece. No film is fast enough to capture these crystalline moments; the eye and brain do.

The eye-brain team does more than just see and record the images presented by the telescope. The eye and brain work in ways unknown to *add* and *subtract* information about the scene. Optical illusions illustrate this characteristic. Almost everyone has seen spots that did not exist in those geometrical grids that confound the eye. In some cases, the eye and brain "integrate" or automatically "interpret" what they see. Astronauts in orbit have seen trains, roads, and wakes of ships on the earth below that at first seemed beyond the eye's power. Later, tests on earth showed how incredibly sensitive the eye and brain are to linear structures. The power of the eye-brain combination is phenomenal but foolable; and both attributes are important in following the canal story.

The tale begins in 1877, when Mars and earth approached one another closely in what is termed a "favorable opposition." Every few years, when these oppositions occur and Mars ventures as close as 35,000,000 miles, almost all suitable telescopes turn toward the red planet. So it was in 1877 as astronomers sought to improve the surface maps that had been made during previous oppositions.

Two things made this opposition a memorable one. First, the American astronomer Asaph Hall, working at the U.S. Naval Observatory, decided to search for Martian satellites. None had ever been found but some astronomers had a hunch that there should be some. Hall's efforts were not quickly rewarded and as summer waned he prepared to abandon his search. Then his wife prevailed on him to try one more night. On that night, August 11, 1887, he found a tiny moonlet orbiting very close to the Martian surface. On the 17th, he found still another. Just why these satellites (named Phobos and Deimos) eluded discovery before this is a puzzle that touches on the canal problem in a strange way. Phobos and Deimos are so tiny (just a few miles in diameter), so close to the planet's surface, and so utterly different from other solar-system moons that a few imaginative souls have suggested that they are artificial objects launched by Martians prior to the 1877 opposition or possibly left there by litterbug visitors. Surely any Martians capable of launching such monstrous satellites into orbit could easily build the canals that made their public debut at the same time.

"Public debut" is proper terminology because a few astronomers had recognized the existence of fine lines on Mars some years before 1877. A Reverend Dawes drew some on his 1864 map of Mars. Nevertheless, to Giovanni Schiaparelli goes the credit for bringing the canals to the attention of the public and the scientific community. The situation is reminiscent of the discovery of sunspot cycles and Jupiter's Great Red Spot when the fame went to the publicizer, not to the finder.

The names of Schiaparelli and the Martian canals are virtually inseparable. Schiaparelli graduated from Turin University in 1854 and studied under Johann Encke in Germany and Friedrich Struve in Russia. He carried out his Martian studies at the Brera Observatory in Milan. All his brilliant work on meteors, Mercury, Venus, and the rest of the solar system, pale beside his more sensational work on the canals. Studying Mars through a nine-inch refracting telescope, he saw his first canals in 1877 while making a high precision map of the Martian surface. In the opposition of 1881–1882, though Mars was farther away, seeing was outstanding and areas that had seemed obscure in 1877 came into focus, revealing (to Schiaparelli, at least) many fine lines that seemed connected in a complicated pattern. Some lines that had seemed single in 1877 now were double—"twinning" or gemination had occurred. Schiaparelli had found the canals and also two of their most frustrating features, the habits of coming and going and of twinning. What solid physical feature on a planet's surface could undergo such metamorphosis? Perhaps it was all in Schiaparelli's head.

In Schiaparelli's words, this is what he saw: "All the vast extent of the continents is furrowed upon every side by a network of fine lines or fine stripes of a more or less pronounced dark color. . . . They traverse the planet for long distances in regular lines, that do not at all resemble the winding courses of our streams. Some of the shorter ones do not attain 300 miles; others extend for thousands. . . . Some are easy to see; others are extremely difficult, and resemble the finest thread of a spider's web drawn across its disk." This description of the telescopic appearance of the canals has not changed much since 1877. Bigger telescopes cannot halt our turbulent atmosphere.

Schiaparelli was undoubtedly impressed by the artificial appearance of his canal drawings but he was careful to refrain from jumping to conclusions. He called his lines "canali," which means primarily "channels" or "grooves" in Italian. In English translation, "canali" became "canals" with all the artificial connotations of the word. It was this connotation that saved the paper that Schiaparelli presented to the Royal Academy of the Lynxes in Rome from obscurity and death in musty files.

The wide publication of Schiaparelli's maps showing a vast interconnected network of "canali" let loose a flood of popular emotion. For hundreds of years, from the time that the other planets were recognized as brethren of the earth circling the same sun, man's imagination had peopled them with intelligent beings, most frequently other men. The canals seemed to be *direct* evidence of other intelligence and, by inference, other men. They confirmed philosophical speculations; they comforted men who felt alone in a universe that the growing science of astronomy had made so huge and foreign.

Popular books about Mars, its inhabitants, and their great waterways, rolled off the presses. The eager public read *The Planet Mars, a Second Earth,* by Professor Jakob Schmick. The whole affair recalls the flying saucer furor in the early 1950s. Perhaps the best gauge of public attitude toward Mars was the 1900 establishment of the Pierre Guzman prize of 100,000 gold francs by Madame Clara Goguet to be paid to the man who first communicated with a star *other than Mars.* It seemed that Mars was thought to be *too easy* a target to qualify for such a prize. Such was the legacy of Schiaparelli.

Schiaparelli assumed a rather objective stance on the question of canals: "Their singular aspect has led some to see in them the work of intelligent beings. I am very careful not to combat this supposition, which contains nothing impossible." In the light of today's science, the Martian canals seem less artificial than they did in Schiaparelli's day, but his carefully chosen words are still appropriate. There are still many who *believe* or fervently *wish* Mars to be populated.

How did the scientific community react to Schiaparelli's observations and the imaginings of the general public? Many deplored the hypothesis of intelligent life as unnecessary and unwarranted, while others looked for purely physical explanations. More evidence was needed. During the 1881–1882 opposition, Henry Perrotin at Nice and A. Stanley Williams in England saw not only the canals but also the twinning effect discovered by Schiaparelli during this particularly favorable observation period. Another surprise came when the dark areas of Mars were observed to become darker during the spring as the polar caps melted, and lighter during the winter as the ice caps re-formed. A few clouds were seen, but Mars seemed mostly desert. Schiaparelli also noticed that round spots existed where several canals intersected. Following the watery nomenclature, he called these spots "lakes," and this time there could be no confusion in translation—Schiaparelli definitely thought there was water on Mars. During the opposition of 1892, the American astronomer William H. Pickering found that even smaller spots could be seen where two canals crossed. He called the spots "oases," which brought visions of Martian deserts spotted with verdant tree-sheltered water sources. Pickering, incidentally, believed that even the moon supported life and it is not surprising to find him on the life-side of the bitter canal controversy that was building up pressure.

The Schiaparelli period ended about the turn of the century. We know few more basic facts about the canals today, but our outlook is quite different. In 1900 most educated laymen believed in a Mars populated by intelligent beings, who were fighting desiccation by making efficient use of their limited water supplies through an immense canal system. The whole idea of Martians reshaping their entire planet to ensure survival fitted right in with the Victorian belief that man was the master of his fate.

Scientists were more cautious but there was not enough data to build alternative hypotheses that sounded reasonable. There were still many astronomers who had never seen the canals. In 1897 J. Joly, in a paper for the Royal Dublin Society, claimed the canals were really ridges caused by the gravitational attraction of asteroids passing close and nearly horizontal to the planet surface prior to impact. Schiaparelli proposed that the canals might be natural cracks in the planetary surface caused by conventional geological forces. One model had Mars covered with water and thickly growing seaweed of different colors; the canals were lines where the seaweed was parted by swift currents. It was difficult to find natural explanations for the geometric precision of the Martian canals. The hypothesis of intelligent life was not completely unreasonable.

Compare the 1900 canal situation with the flying saucer craze fifty years later. Something is seen, but reproducible facts are not sufficient to build really strong models or hypotheses. Imagination is given free rein and controversy rages. The same kinds of battles are being fought over the nature of quasars but on a more objective basis. Controversy is really part of the scientific method. Things get out of hand only when extraterrestrial life, extrasensory perception, evolution, and similar frontier areas are involved. Scientists can say almost anything about inaccessible atoms and stars, but the moment life—intelligent life, particularly—is mentioned, laymen, faddists, and cultists enter the lists and the war spreads to the newspapers, the pulpit, and tv.

The Martian canal battle was kindled by Percival Lowell in the first decade of this century. His factual ammunition was not noticeably superior to that of Schiaparelli but he aimed his guns with devasting effect. Lowell was a man with a mission, and his work with the Martian canals affects the attitude of science toward them even today. His story is curious and fraught with irrationality and illogic.

Percival Lowell was hardly a bona fide member of the astronomical fraternity, but he had an impressive background. He was a Harvard man and one of the aristocratic Boston Lowells. Amy Lowell, the poetess, was his sister; and his brother became a president of Harvard University. His genealogy was so impressive that some English publications called him *Sir* Percival Lowell. Whatever his pedigree, he was not formally educated or trained as an astronomer. What he did have was money.

After his graduation from Harvard, Lowell traveled and dabbled in business, much as we would expect of an independently wealthy young American of the Victorian era. Then he read Schiaparelli's accounts of his Martian researches and he became a man transformed. Instead of putting his wealth in yachts or seaside mansions he built the Lowell Observatory in the high, clean, clear air of Flagstaff, Arizona. As soon as his observatory opened, in 1894, he began his studies of Mars. Thus commenced the Lowell era of Martian canal history.

Percival Lowell must be acknowledged as a talented man and a crack astronomer and mathematician despite his layman upbringing and patrician ways. He predicted the position of Pluto (he called it Planet X) from its perturbations of Uranus, but failed to find it himself. (Coincidentally, tiny Pluto was finally picked out from among hundreds of thousands of surrounding stars in 1920 by Clyde Tombaugh at Lowell Observatory. Tombaugh is an astronomer who also figures strongly in today's discussions of Mars.)

Blessed by clear air and a good telescope (a 24-inch reflector), Lowell drew maps of the Martian surface in far greater detail than those of his predecessor, Schiaparelli. He mapped hundreds of canals and saw that some actually penetrated into the dark areas of Mars. When Lowell perceived the canals darkening along with the planet's dark areas during the Martian spring, he was convinced that water was flowing along them from the poles, giving life to wide strips of vegetation along the canal sides. The vegetation made the canal regions visible much as the Nile River would be "magnified" to an astronaut by its cultivated areas. The straightness, precision, twinning, and network organization of the canals inferred artificiality. The public had been well prepared for Lowell's first book by Schiaparelli and almost twenty years of speculation in the popular press. *Mars* was published in 1895 by Houghton, Mifflin & Co. in Boston. *Mars and Its Canals,* published in 1900, refined the Intelligent Martians model even further, and was much more influential.

The Lowell model of Mars was not very different from, or any more extreme than, the life-on-Mars models described earlier. His story seemed to hang together better; it was better organized and more convincing. Lowell's picture of an intelligent race striving to survive on a water-scarce planet struck a responsive chord in the human organism. The public marveled at the thousand-mile long canals that carried the planet's life blood to Martian cities across the deserts of this old and probably dying neighbor in the skies. If rockets were available to send water to the thirsty Martians, popular subscription would have easily collected enough money to do the job.

Besides inducing pangs of sympathy for the struggling Martians, Lowell's writing stirred still another emotion: the desire for a peaceful, united planet. Lowell believed that the Martians had raised civilization to new heights and had organized their entire planet in their struggle against nature. In *Mars and Its Canals,* he wrote: "War is a survival among us from savage times and affects now chiefly the boyish and unthinking element of the nation. The wisest realize that there are better ways for practicing heroism and other and more certain ends of ensuring survival of the fittest. It is something people outgrow." These words, so reminiscent of H. G. Wells's idealism, must have gained him many followers regardless of the fact that his hypothesis was unconfirmed.

Lowell's model of Mars seemed quite reasonable to many astronomers, save for the part about the presence of intelligent life. Many astronomers had seen the canals and verified much of what Lowell saw; some used the Flagstaff instrument and worked closely with Lowell. Mars looked like an earth which, because of its distance from the sun, was cold, dry and past its prime.

Many other scientists, though, would have nothing to do with Lowell and his Martian waterways. Two unscientific counterattacks were possible (as they are today when science wants to scuttle someone who breaks ranks), namely, ridicule and simple denial of whatever is seen. Ridicule did not stop Lowell and, because he was independently wealthy, he felt his position in the scientific community was secondary to his main mission: Mars. Outright denial of Martian canals, however, was a different kind of attack, one which was made more serious when Lowell reported seeing lines (he did not call them canals) on Mercury, Venus, and some of Jupiter's satellites. He utilized Mercury's markings to determine its (correct) period of rotation. Lowell's "cartwheel" effect on Venus is now in accord with one model of this planet's atmospheric structure. No one else saw lines on these spheres and some of the best observers in the world still saw no canals on Mars. Asaph Hall, who found Deimos and Phobos after everyone else failed, could not see the canals. Neither could American astronomers Edward Barnard nor George Hale, both with superior instruments. Astronomers in northern Europe were unable to see the canals. Many stated flatly that they did not exist. They were honest about it; perhaps the poor seeing in their area was the cause.

One scientist who was certain Lowell was a fake was Alfred Russel Wallace, the English naturalist who conceived the theory of evolution along with Darwin. Wallace was asked to write a review of Lowell's books. As he read about the Martians struggling to conserve their dwindling water supplies, he was outraged by Lowell's theory. The book review ballooned into a book entitled: *Is Mars Habitable?* (London, 1907). Wallace jumped from natural history into planetary physics and stated that all scientists knew that Mars was too cold to sustain life and that there was *no water there at all.* Mars, according to Wallace, was "absolutely uninhabitable." Wallace was erroneous and most unscientific in his reports of temperature and water. It was a good illustration of what the idea of life on Mars did to logic and rationality. One happy by-product of Wallace's attack was the wide promulgation of his thought that the canals might be due to cracks in Mars' mantle due to shrinking of the core.

A less extreme position was taken by the optical-illusion forces. Lowell and the others who claimed to see canals actually saw something, most likely dots, streaks, and smudges that their eye and brain integrated into straight lines. Something was on Mars but it was the eye-brain combination that made the artificial-looking canals. A celebrated experiment supported the optical-illusion position. In 1903 E. W. Maunder, an English astronomer, showed a group of schoolboys some drawings of Mars with a few dots replacing the canals. In copying the drawings from a distance, many of the boys added sharp, linear canals. Obviously, the purported canal networks were illusory. Lowell had faith in his first-hand observations and ignored the "small boy theory" as he called it. Another

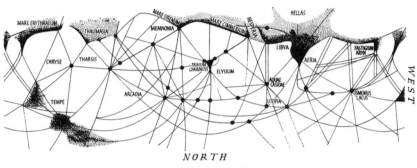

MARS-1901

A Mercator Projection of Mars by Lowell showing the major canals as he saw them. The black dots are the oases. Many of the curved canals in this projection actually follow great circle routes. If one accepts such a map of the canals, one is almost forced to accept also their artificiality. Lowell's detailed maps show about 700 canals.

English astronomer, Patrick Moore, tells in his book *Guide to Mars* (Frederick Muller, London, 1965) how he repeated Maunder's experiment in 1950 using disconnected dots and streaks instead of canals. The results were much less convincing than those of Maunder. Such tests remind one of present-day "experiments" with balloons and other flying objects that are supposed to evoke "sightings" of flying saucers. If there really are linear arrays of spots and streaks on the Martian surface, something has to account for their nicely geometric arrangement.

The Martian canals may *actually* be linear collections of spots and streaks, as recent developments show. The problem of canal "existence," though, did not have to wait long for an answer. Some of the largest canals finally showed up as wispy streaks on photographs taken by E. C. Slipher in 1921. Laymen, too, kept seeing canals, even with small telescopes, and always in the same places. Visual acuity seems a certain factor, as do instrument quality and location. Modern astronomers are quite willing to admit that the canals are real, though probably not continuous surface features. Most of the smoke from the battles of the Lowell period has cleared away, and new facts have forced all extremists to move toward a middle ground.

Lowell forced astronomers to examine Mars more closely than any other planet, and that was beneficial to all of science. Percival Lowell died at Flagstaff November 12, 1916. The battle he started is still joined but everyone seems more temperate—and perhaps science as a whole looks a little more kindly on Percival Lowell in spite of those disputatious books he wrote. The telescope at Lowell Observatory still searches the clear Arizona skies and has an enviable scientific record. The Mars books and the Observatory are fitting memorials for an unusual man.

World War I silenced the canal controversy and it was never renewed by a champion with Lowell's vigor, evangelism, and the personal wealth needed to carry on research against the consensus of established scientific opinion. In the twenties popular books still trumpeted the Lowell position, mainly because it helped sell more copies, *not* because any new evidence had been uncovered. New evidence refuting or supporting Lowell was hard to obtain. The visibility of planetary details is limited by the vagaries of our atmosphere and the acuity of the observer, not the size of the telescope. Lowell and his contemporaries were working at the limits already, and this is one reason why observers the world over could not always duplicate his canal drawings. Only a little grist has been added to the mill since Lowell died.

Audouin Dollfus, the French astronomer, has been a student of Mars for many years. In 1948 he published a paper in *Comptes Rendus* describing how he saw some of the Martian canals break up into irregular discontinuous spots while he was watching them. Seeing details within the canal structure represents a higher order of observation than seeing the canals in the first place; something like discovering that the nucleus of an atom is composed of subatomic particles. Dollfus was using a 24-inch refracting telescope (the same size as Lowell's) at the Pic du Midi, in the French

Pyrenees. His observatory is at an altitude of about 10,000 feet, giving him seeing conditions at least the equal of Lowell's. Dollfus has classified the canals into three groups:

1. Wide, shady, band-like structures.
2. Narrow, more regular streaks.
3. Thread-like, perfectly black, artificial-looking lines.

It is the lines of the last category that Dollfus has seen break up into spots and patches under ideal seeing conditions. Even more significant in the light of the pictures of a heavily cratered Mars taken by the Mariner-4 space probe is the fact that Dollfus and his collaborators have succeeded in seeing similar fine structure (spots and patches) within the dark areas of Mars. Banded structures on the lunar surface break up into similar fine structure when high-power telescopes are turned on them. And we know from Mariner 4 that the Martian surface seems much like that of the moon. Lines of spots cry for explanation almost as much as continuous grooves or "canali," though they do not bring visions of heroic Martians fighting desperately to husband their precious water supplies.

Another aspect of the canals that has been singled out in recent years is their variability—not just whether they are or are not seen—but structural and darkness changes. G. de Vaucouleurs has given two well-verified examples that must be accounted for by any canal hypothesis. The canal Nepenthes-Thoth is notorious for its fickleness. It was faint and narrow in 1939; it seemed to be double in 1941 (the gemination phenomenon); and appeared as a broad, dark belt in 1958. This variation, seen often in the past, has been confirmed repeatedly by photography. Something is happening on Mars and *not* in the earth's atmosphere or the mind of the observer.

De Vaucouleurs has also rediscovered the canal Erinnys that was seen and mapped by Schiaparelli but then disappeared from Martian maps (even Lowell's) for sixty years. Since 1941, when de Vaucouleurs first noted its reappearance, Erinnys has become very dark and conspicuous. An associated oasis is brand new, appearing on none of the older maps. Martian canals come and go like the Great Red Spot of Jupiter. Planetary markings are far from static, and possibly there may be a common stimulus that we can only guess at.

Another recently verified Martian peculiarity is the occasional appearance of bright "flares" on Mars. Historically, the flares are rare, but Japanese astronomers reported several in 1958. The flares generally last for just a few minutes and then disappear. Cloud formation often follows the flare. Many scientists interpret the flares as large volcanic eruptions on Mars. If Mars is indeed still active in the volcanic sense, drifting ashes may somehow be caught by natural canal-like formations and increase their visibility. (Flares also occur on the moon. This subject will be covered more fully in Chapter 10.)

Short of going to Mars is there any other way to determine canal artificiality or contrivance? Snowflakes, mudflat crack patterns, cracks around volcanic craters, and many other purely natural phenomena have a degree of regularity about them that might mislead a distant observer into thinking they were artificial. When a network of interconnected lines exists, a branch of mathematics called *topology* gives us a way of measuring the "degree of connectedness." The higher the degree of connectedness the more paths there are between intersection points, and the more freely commerce, water, or whatever may flow between intersections. In a network conceived by intelligent beings, the intersections are, of course, cities, telephone switching centers, and the like. In other words, intelligent beings intentionally provide many interconnections. The aim of network analysis is the measurement and comparison of the degrees of connectedness of natural networks, manmade networks, and the Martian canal system. W. A. Webb presented the results of such an analysis at the 1961 Washington meeting of the International Astronautical Federation. He showed that the Martian canals had about the same degree of connectedness as the Iowa and Ohio railroad systems, and that it was much higher than natural cracks found in lava, glazes, and limestone. Of course, such statistics are suggestive, but they prove nothing. There may be natural crack phenomena occurring on Mars that reveal much more organization than the earthly examples chosen for comparison.

The following "contemporary consensus" about Mars and its canals is opposed by both the canal cult and the canal skeptics for it fits neither extreme.

Mars is cold and dry. Some small amount of water is present. Temperatures at the equator sometimes rise well above the freezing point of water. A thin atmosphere is present, containing carbon dioxide but probably very little oxygen. Surface atmospheric pressure is only 1% to 2% of that on earth. Clouds of various sorts have been observed. The Martian surface is thought to be quite flat and, as Mariner 4 has shown, well cratered. The polar caps are now thought to be water, perhaps in the form of hoarfrost, or carbon dioxide as dry ice, and when the caps melt, the blue-green patches and canal regions grow dark as the spring "wave of quickening" moves toward the equator. The spectrum of the dark regions of Mars shows some suspicious similarities to that expected from vegetation but also to other substances, such as deuterium.

As for the canals, most astronomers would subscribe to the following list of statements:

1. The canals (or "cracks") exist; few argue this anymore.
2. Some canals are double and gemination occurs.
3. Oases exist at canal intersections.
4. The canals are connected in a network, but not necessarily a continuous or contrived one.
5. The visibility of the canals changes with the season.
6. The canals cannot be waterways, because of the scarcity of water on mars.

Telescopic observations alone have led to the above conclusions. How much more did the photographs taken by Mariner 4 add to the picture? As Mariner 4 passed within 8300 miles of the Martian surface on July 15, 1965, it took a series of sixteen pictures of the Martian surface with a television-type camera. This series of pictures showed a heavily cratered planet whose surface complexion resembled that of the moon. A few scientists had predicted a cratered Mars, but the final pictures were none the less startling, especially to those thinking in terms of Lowell's deserts, dark-green vegetated areas, and system of immense irrigation canals. Mariner 4 radioed back images of a seemingly lifeless, arid, pockmarked hulk of a planet. The initial analyses performed by scientists at the Jet Propulsion Laboratory at Pasadena indicated that there were no traces of any of the major canals that should have appeared in several of the pictures. It seemed like an overwhelming repudiation of four generations of canal watchers.

In the western melodrama, the cavalry always shows up in the nick of time to save the day. There were many cavalrymen waiting in the wings to rescue the canal hypothesis or at the very least to save the reputations of the hundreds of astronomers who had seen canals with their own eyes. Before conservative astronomers could say "I told you they were never there!" articles appeared pointing

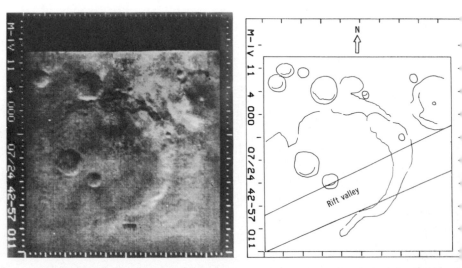

Mariner-4 Photograph No. 11 contrasted with the Burgess sketch of the rift valley seen in the picture. Several Mariner pictures show such "linear features" occurring where canals are observed by telescope. (After E. Burgess, *Spaceflight*, Feb. 1966)

out that several of the Mariner 4 pictures had linear features just where earth-based astronomy had located canals. Eric Burgess in his article "There Are 'Canals' on Mars" (*Spaceflight*, February 1966) specifically identifies a well-known canal with what appears to him to be a rift valley (crack) running diagonally on Mariner Photograph No. 11 as shown. Burgess claims that other pictures show similar evidence of wide-scale planet fracturing. Apparently from a distance, these rift valleys stand out rather vividly against the background of craters and other surface irregularities just as roads do for an astronaut. To the layman, these rift valley walls are not obvious but comparison of the Mariner photograph and the Burgess drawing do reveal the presence of parallel escarpments, which calculation shows are separated by about thirty miles. No one contends that they see the work of intelligent beings in the Mariner pictures.

In the light of ninety years of telescopic study and sixteen space-probe pictures, what are the Martian canals? The answer has to be that no one knows for sure but the list of possibilities has been pared down considerably. There are two kinds of hypotheses that must be mated to form a viable canal model. First, one must postulate a mechanism (usually geological) that can create long, straight, intersecting surface features. Second, one must produce a scheme for giving the surface features varying visibility from earthly telescopes.

Taking the problem of creating surface features first, there is a choice of: linear chains of volcanoes; long, igneous "dikes" of molten rock forced up through the Martian surface; linear patterns of meteorite craters (possibly caused by meteor swarms); planet-wide surface fracture patterns due to the impact of huge asteroids; and linear crustal faults caused by natural crustal adjustments during planetary cooling. Based on terrestrial experience, a network of linear features seems most likely to be caused by faulting and fracturing processes.

A number of inorganic chemical and biological phenomena have been suggested that would make surface features visible as the Martian seasons change. If Mars does boast numerous volcanoes (as the observed flares might suggest), the ashes from eruptions could collect in low spots; volcanoes, however, are unlikely to be seasonal in nature. More likely are the hypotheses stating that low areas on the Martian surface may contain water, water vapor, and/or heavy gases, and in addition may be substantially warmer than surrounding high areas. Chemical changes in surface compounds might occur as supplies of moisture and various gases change with the seasons. The same thinking applies to vegetable forms of life which might well occur in pockets and rift valleys. One thing is sure, telescopic study from earth is unlikely to reveal which of these choices (if any) is the correct one.

Even though purely natural causes are favored nowadays in explaining the Martian canals, the evidence still might be stretched to admit artificial canals. The rift valleys seen by some in the Mariner 4 pictures could be ancient, highly eroded and cratered artificial waterways built eons ago when Mars still possessed abundant water. This hypothesis is most unlikely, but the believers in intelligent life on Mars will never be convinced one way or the other until men finally land on the planet itself either to find no Martians at all or to be taken to their leader.

This brings us to the subject of preparing for the ultimate voyage to Mars. Undoubtedly, there will be numerous unmanned space probes sent to Mars prior to risking astronauts. NASA is planning more Mariner "fly-by" probes, but they will have only a few hours in the vicinity of the planet in which to make their measurements. More pictures from other parts of Mars would be very welcome, however. Mars orbiters and landers would come next. The orbiters could survey much of the planet with tv cameras after the fashion of the Tiros and Nimbus weather satellites. Landers braking to soft landings in dark areas and even the canals themselves (after all, they are tens and sometimes hundreds of miles wide) could carry out measurements of the chemical and physical environments. Life detection instruments would be high priority cargo. (See Chapter 11.) NASA hopes to carry out such experiments within the next decade or two in its Voyager Program. Despite the versatility of unmanned instrument packages, they may be unable to detect such a subtle thing as life. The Martian surface may be so different from what we expect that our naive experiments may not encompass all facets of it. A camera on the Martian surface might not perceive such large-scale features as the canals.

It will be the manned trips to Mars, beginning in the 1980s, that will probably settle the canal question once and for all. As the disk of Mars begins to fill the spacecraft's observing port, astronauts will be able to see how the surface features change with distance. They may see well-defined canals from 100,000 miles out, only to see them dissolve into craters and surface formations as they pass the 10,000-mile mark. Once on the ground, geologists can go to work on the "linear features" some have seen in the 1965 Mariner pictures, while other scientists make chemical and biological studies of the surface. Of course, if the astronauts splash down in one of the canals, Lowell will be vindicated in a most spectacular fashion.

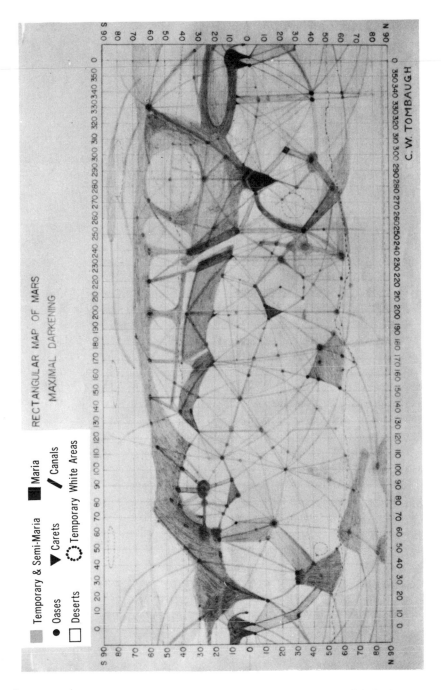

RECTANGULAR MAP OF MARS

MAXIMAL DARKENING

C. W. TOMBAUGH

Temporary & Semi-Maria ■ Maria

• Oases ▼ Carets / Canals

□ Deserts ⟲ Temporary White Areas

Clyde Tombaugh's map of Mars does not show the draftsman-like precision of Lowell's maps and conveys the fuzzy character of planetary images in the telescope.

READING LIST

AMERICAN INSTITUTE OF AERONAUTICS AND ASTRONAUTICS. *AIAA/AAS Stepping Stones to Mars Meeting*, AIAA, New York, 1966.

ASIMOV, I. *Asimov's Biographical Encyclopedia of Science and Technology*, Doubleday & Company, New York, 1964.

BRANLEY, F. M. *Mars, Planet Number Four*, Thomas Y. Crowell Company, New York, 1962.

GLASSTONE, S. *Sourcebook on the Space Sciences*, D. Van Nostrand Company, Princeton, 1965.

HALL, J. S. *The Photographic Story of Mars*, Sky Publishing Company, Cambridge, 1962.

LEY, W. *Watchers of the Skies*, The Viking Press, New York, 1963.

———, and VON BRAUN, W. *The Exploration of Mars*, The Viking Press, New York, 1956.

LOWELL, P. *Mars*, Houghton, Mifflin, Boston, 1895.

MOORE, P. *Guide to Mars*, Frederick Muller, London, 1965.

MORGANTHALER, G. W., ed. *Exploration of Mars*, Western Periodicals Co., North Hollywood, 1963.

WHIPPLE, F. L. *Earth, Moon, and Planets*, Harvard University Press, Cambridge, 1963.

9

THE CASE OF
THE MISSING PLANET

The Soviet astronomer S. V. Orlov has estimated that over a *quarter billion* chunks of rock with dimensions greater than a half-mile swarm through interplanetary space. The overwhelming majority of this "debris" plies an orbital course around the sun in the huge 350,000,000-mile gap between Mars and Jupiter. This is the "asteroid belt." Errant fragments of this belt penetrate all reaches of the solar system and undoubtedly collide with the planets on occasion. The asteroid Hermes, for example, flashed past the earth in January 1938 only 485,000 miles away—twice the distance of the moon. A collision with a rock a few miles in diameter at speeds of several tens of thousands of miles per hour would probably shatter the rocky crust of the earth as if it were an eggshell. It is not a very likely occurrence, but the possibility underscores the destructive potentialities of asteroids. Fortunately, they have beneficial aspects, too.

In the asteroid population there are a quarter billion clues about the origin of the solar system. If we could catch one and chemically and geologically analyze it, it would greatly enhance our knowledge of what happened in the cataclysm that led to the formation of the belt. Asteroids are, in a sense, messengers from beyond Mars. Just by studying the orbits of the asteroids we can learn a great deal about what has happened to the solar system in the last few billion years. Some asteroid enthusiasts have even contemplated sidling up to an asteroid with a rocket, dropping off instruments or even a human colony, and letting the asteroid carry this cargo around the solar system as a sort of natural-born spaceship.

From the standpoint of physical theories and models, the discovery of the asteroids presents the fascinating tale of scientists employing a law with apparently no physical basis whatever to plan their experiments. Or is there something after all to the famous (or infamous) Bode's Law?

Sometimes nature seems awry and our intuition and common sense tell us that either the hand of the Grand Architect trembled or we are not seeing all there is to see. That immense and unseemly gap in distance between Mars and Jupiter bothered many early astronomers. There *should* be a planet there, but nothing could be found. The great Johann Kepler, who was a mystic and renowned astrologer as well as an astronomer and mathematician, also "felt" that there must be some unseen body circling the sun between Mars and Jupiter. There was a "hole" in the planetary pattern that he was trying to "explain" with various geometric shapes nesting inside one another. Intuition was given mathematical substance in 1772 when Johann Titius, a professor of mathematics and physics at the University of Wittenberg, published an empirical law that gave not only the distance of all known planets but some that had not been found. In essence, Titius composed a series of numbers that by coincidence (supposedly) were the same as the planetary distances. Here is the equation:

$$a = 0.4 + 0.3 \times 2^n$$

The quantity "a" is the planet's average distance from the sun measured in Astronomical Units (A.U.)—(units equal to the earth's distance from the sun, about 93,000,000 miles). The quantity "n" starts at $-\infty$ for Mercury, goes to 0 for Venus, 1 for earth, 2 for Mars, and so on, increasing by one for the other planets. Application of the equation matched the distances of the known planets remarkably well; so well that there were suppositions that the Titius equation was the manifestation of some unknown astronomical law. The table below compares computed and measured planetary radii:

	n	PLANET DISTANCES FROM SUN IN A.U.	
		TITIUS EQUATION	OBSERVED
Mercury	—∞	0.4	0.39
Venus	0	0.7	0.72
Earth	1	1.0	1.00
Mars	2	1.6	1.52
?	3	2.8	?
Jupiter	4	5.2	5.20
Saturn	5	10.0	9.55
?	6	19.6	?
?	7	38.8	?
?	8	77.2	?

Such astonishing success by an empirical law fanned speculation about the missing data. If Titius's mathematical relationship had a physical basis, such as some law dictating the formation of a star's planet system, the question marks should represent real planets that had not yet been observed. Since the Titius law says nothing about planet size, the missing planets might be so small that they could easily escape notice. On the other hand, if the equation was merely a fortuitous quirk, an accidental mirroring of reality by a chance series of numbers, the question marks meant nothing at all.

It was Johann Bode, editor of the *Astronomisches Jahrbuch,* who publicized the Titius relationship. Although Bode eventually became director of the Berlin Observatory and the author of a huge star catalog, he is remembered mostly for his popularization of this single equation. The Titius equation became the Bode-Titius Law and, even more frequently, Bode's Law. In the light of what ultimately happened, Titius would probably have been happy that his name was severed from the law.

One of the most significant tests of a physical law is its ability to predict. For a while, it looked as if Bode's Law (as it will now be called) did have some basis in physical reality. In 1781, the German-English astronomer William Herschel discovered the planet Uranus at a distance of 19.2 A.U. from the sun, just where Bodes' Law said it would be. In those times, this was as noteworthy a find as a confirmation of Einstein's General Theory of Relativity would be today. Here was a law that worked, though its physical basis was unknown, and the rush to find more new planets began. Planet hunting became the major occupation of nineteenth century astronomy.

That a hole in the pattern of planets existed between Mars and Jupiter was now confirmed by a "proven" equation. Intuition and mysticism had been replaced by logic, or at least by orderly speculation.

By 1800, many astronomers were searching the plane of the ecliptic, the great circle of the celestial sphere, with their telescopes for the "hidden" planet at 2.8 A.U. One searcher was the Baron von Zach, the court astronomer of Duke Ernst of Saxe-Gotha. Von Zach had been convinced of the correctness of Bode's Law by the discovery of Uranus and had directed his efforts accordingly. He quickly recognized, however, that a thorough search was beyond the capabilities of a single astronomer. To solve this problem he convened a group of six fellow astronomers in the town of Lillienthal in the fall of 1800, proposing the formation of a team of twenty-four astronomers to accurately map as many sections of the zodiac. During the mapping, each observer would keep his eyes peeled for the missing planet. Von Zach's suggestion made sense, particularly since the whole astronomical fraternity was intrigued by the Mars-Jupiter gap and Bode's Law. Letters describing the contemplated project were dispatched to other astronomers.

One of the letters was sent to Father Giuseppe Piazzi at Palermo, but before it reached him he had achieved the main objective of the project. While revising a star catalog on January 1, 1801, Piazzi discerned a small star in Taurus that was not recorded in his catalog. By the next night, the star had shifted noticeably. The same thing happened the following night. The new object could not be a star, and Piazzi supposed that it might be a tailless comet. He announced his find in letters to the Italian astronomer Oriani and to Bode in Berlin. As soon as von Zach and his committee, who called themselves the "celestial police," heard about the Piazzi discovery they realized that the ambitious zodiac project was no longer necessary. Piazzi had forwarded enough data for them to see that the new object's orbit was definitely not that of a comet but instead seemed to be that of a circle at 2.8 A.U., just where Bode's Law said the new planet would be.

Unfortunately, Piazzi had fallen ill before he had taken enough data for the computation of a precise orbit. By the time he had recovered, his discovery, "Object Piazzi," had left the night sky. The temporary loss of Object Piazzi turned out to be a substantial gain for mathematics. Johann Karl Friedrich Gauss, a 24-year-old German mathematician, read of Piazzi's finding in the astronomical magazine that von Zach edited. Gauss believed that there *was* enough data to calculate a better orbit, given the right mathematical tools. New mathematical tools were a Gauss specialty, and he promptly invented the famous "method of least squares" to handle the orbit computations. Using the ephemeris, the astronomical almanac Gauss made up, Heinrich Olbers was able to find Object Piazzi again precisely one year to the day after the original discovery.

Olbers continued to follow Object Piazzi in order to provide Gauss with additional orbital data. On March 28, 1802, in the same celestial neighborhood as Object Piazzi, he came upon a second small, planet-like object. This also proved an occupant of the Mars-Jupiter gap and a supporter of Bode's Law. The first two of the quarter billion chunks of rock postulated by Orlov had been found.

A problem in terminology now arose. It was easy enough to name the discoveries of Piazzi and Olbers—*Ceres* and *Pallas*—but what kind of astronomical objects were they? Not full-fledged planets, obviously. Herschel ventured the name "asteroid" because they were points of light like stars. Piazzi wanted "planetoid" or "cometoid" because their motion across the celestial sphere was either planet-like or comet-like. Now that we know better, planetoid seems most appropriate, but asteroid is still used most often in the literature.

Since the new planetoids were apparently considered smaller than any "classical" planet, everyone began to surmise about their origin. Thus, today's two major planetoid hypotheses were born immediately after the discovery of Ceres and Pallas. In 1802, Olbers suggested in a letter to Bode that Ceres and Pallas were pieces remaining after a larger planet had exploded. Others thought that perhaps the primordial planet-stuff, strewn about the solar system during its formation, had failed to coalesce into a planet in the gap between Mars and Jupiter.

By 1816 Vesta and Juno had been added to the planetoid rolls. Were there more? Olbers thought not, though some small splinters from the original explosion might be floating around in space invisible to earthlings. Olbers and others stopped looking. It was not until 1845 that Karl Hencke, a German post office official, whose

hobby was astronomy, found number five, Astraea. Two years later
he located another, Hebe. Still, planetoid discovery was a time-
consuming, painstaking business and new ones came slowly. By the
end of 1850, only thirteen were recognized. More and more astronomers began to look for planetoids, most likely for the renown
connected with the discovery, for there was little astronomical value
to merely extending the growing list. The list lengthened as more
and better telescopes sifted through the stars in the vicinity of the
asteroid belt looking for points of light that moved rapidly against
the background of the fixed stars. By 1890 over three hundred planetoids were registered.

Keeping track of this parade of tiny objects took a lot of work.
Ephemeris calculation itself was backbreaking labor, and what
did all the columns of figures prove? The Germans started the first
clearing house for planetoid data in an attempt to control the *Kleine
Planetenplage* (plague of the minor planets).

The deluge continued. With telescope alone, Johann Palisa, in
Vienna, located fifty-three new planetoids. But his record was sur-
passed by Professor Max Wolf at Heidelberg, who was extraordinarily successful with a new photographic technique that he per-
fected in 1891 for picking out planetoids from amongst the star
background. Wolf found 228 planetoids. His technique was simple:
He placed a photographic plate at the focal plane of the telescope
and drove the telescope at the same rate as the movement of the
fixed stars. By this method, after a time exposure, the plate shows
the fixed stars as dots, while a planetoid, a major planet, or a comet
announces itself as a streak on the plate.

Success was overwhelming. By 1890, mythological names had
been exhausted, and were supplanted with numbers and a chrono-
logical code. One wonders why it took so long to find these "vermin"
of the skies when now they are such a menace to astronomical research. To illustrate the kind of problem the planetoids created for
the larger telescopes, consider the search the American astronomer
Seth B. Nicholson made for moons for Jupiter. Near Jupiter Nicholson found the tracks of thirty-two small objects that could be either
planetoids or new moons of Jupiter. It took much time and calculation to eliminate each planetoid from consideration.

Despite careful inventories and orbit computations, planetoids
were "lost" on occasion. After all, they were very tiny objects and

frequently moved in eccentric orbits where the gravitational attractions of the major planets threw them off course. One planetoid discoverer, J. C. Watson, wanted to take no chances that his personal planetoid, Andromache, would be lost. He left a sum of money with instructions to keep telescopes trained on Andromache. His money did not prevent its loss, and Andromache was lost between 1877 and 1893.

Enough anecdotes about the planetoid plague; they are there by the millions; it is time to describe their regularities and idiosyncrasies in the light of modern astronomy and try to ascertain their origin. In modern vernacular: What is the big picture?

If one knows exactly where to look, one can see Vesta with the naked eye. All other planetoids are telescopic objects. The "Big Four" were the first to be discovered: Ceres, Pallas, Juno, and Vesta. In size, they are 470, 300, 120, and 240 miles in diameter. Astronomers estimate that there are twelve planetoids with diameters between 100 and 150 miles, and perhaps two hundred with diameters between 50 and 100 miles. Except for the Big Four, these diameters are not measured by the angles the planetoids subtend, but rather from measurements of their brightnesses and distances. Of course, a reflectivity ratio (albedo) must be assumed to make these estimates, and generally an albedo near that of the lunar surface is employed. All the planetoids together probably do not weigh more than one thousandth the mass of the earth. The planetoid parent body, if such there was, was scarcely a planet before its breakup. No one really knows how many small-size planetoids there may be. Except for the small ones that pass dangerously close to earth, they are unseeable. There may be a quarter *billion* as Orlov believes or only a quarter *million*. If Orlov is correct the total planetoid plague may have been the debris of an earth-sized planet.

Seen through the telescope many planetoids seem to twinkle. The usual interpretation is that the multi-mile hunks of rock are irregular in shape and spin slowly in space, displaying different facets to the observer. The reflection of sunlight off the facets causes the twinkling. Twinkling is so common with the smaller planetoids that most are believed to be oblong, slablike, or just rough chunks—about what one would expect of fragments from a collision or explosion. The Big Four planetoids, on the other hand, are apparently rather uniform spheres and this, perhaps, indicates a different history.

Science fiction writers habitually describe planetoids as rough, pitted, and moonlike. Their heroes must clamber over jagged, dusty surfaces in space suits, for there is no air, and take great care that they do not accidentally "jump" off into space never to return. The gravitational attraction of the small planetoids is so minute that a

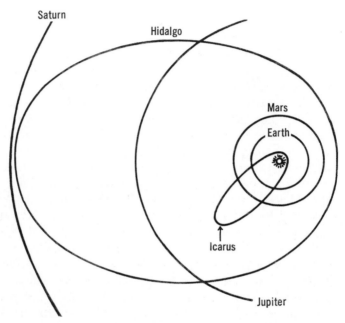

The planetoids Hidalgo and Icarus illustrate the great variety of orbits that has been observed. Icarus penetrates so close to the sun that it is heated red hot.

man could easily achieve escape velocity with only an energetic step. All evidence favors such views of planetoids. In any case, the asteroids seem ideal staging areas for space explorations due to their low gravity—it will be simple to land and take off and little fuel need be expended to break gravitational ties.

If some celestial cataclysm truly created the planetoids, their orbits should reflect the force of the original explosion or collision. The mean diameter of all planetoid orbits taken together is about 2.9 A.U., very close to the 2.8 A.U. foreseen by Bode's Law. The great majority of planetoids orbit the sun in the huge space separating Mars and Jupiter. It is the small minority of planetoids that interests us here, for a few have spread out all over the solar system, not just in the plane of the ecliptic great circle, where the planets lie, but also at angles up to 45° off the ecliptic. Hidalgo and Icarus illustrate the orbital extremes. Hidalgo almost touches the orbit of Saturn at its aphelion (point farthest from the sun); Icarus penetrates past Mars, earth, Venus, and Mercury to within 0.2 A.U. of the sun. Both Hidalgo and Icarus have ends of their ellipses anchored in the Mars-Jupiter gap; conceivably they could both be fragments born in the same explosion.

The orbits of these miniature, moonlike planets display several other peculiarities that gladden the hearts of those who like to play billiards on an interplanetary scale. That monster planet Jupiter gravitationally stirs up the asteroid belt just as it seems to affect the sun itself. (Chapter 6)

Planetoid 588, also called Achilles, the first of the "male" planetoids, discovered February 22, 1906, by Max Wolf, illustrates an unique way in which Jupiter can gravitationally "capture" a planetoid. The first orbital data for Achilles indicated that it was traveling at about eight miles a second in a nearly circular orbit. That was questionable because Jupiter circled the sun at the same speed, and in Newton's view of the solar system all objects traveling at the same speeds in circular orbits are also at the same distance from the sun—regardless of mass. That meant that Achilles might be in the same orbit as Jupiter; the word *might* is necessary because the plane of the planetoid's orbit could be tilted with respect to that of Jupiter. Professor C. V. L. Charlier of Lund Observatory quickly discovered that Achilles was actually in Jupiter's orbit but leading it in its voyage around the sun by 55½°. It was immediately obvious to those who had studied the work of Joseph Louis Lagrange, the Italian-French mathematician, that Achilles was riding around the sun in a gravitational trap created by a combination of the fields of the sun and Jupiter. Lagrange had shown that one particularly simple solution of the notorious "three body problem" occurred when the sun, a large planet such as Jupiter, and an object of negligible mass (Achilles) were located at the vertices of an equilateral triangle. The gravitational pulls of the sun and Jupiter and centrifugal force all canceled out at these two libration (oscillatory balance) points, giving Achilles a force-free haven. Actually, *two* equilateral triangles are possible. Lagrange also showed the existence of several other points of stability in the Jupiter-sun complex that need not concern us further.

Subsequent search of the leading and lagging libration points showed five planetoids in the gravitational pocket ahead of Jupiter and ten behind. More or less accidentally, the planetoids at the libration points began to be named after heroes of the Trojan War. Mythological nomenclature, always so dear to the hearts of the astronomers, became fixed, and all libration-point asteroids became *Trojan* asteroids. Many astronomers suspect that Saturn may occa-

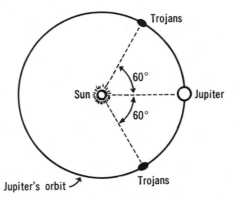

The Trojan groups of planetoids lead and follow Jupiter around the sun. Lagrange showed that the combined gravitational attractions and centrifugal forces create a "trap" that catches planetoids and holds them until Saturn or some other perturbing force ejects them.

sionally gravitationally steal one of the Trojans when it comes close. The cast of characters may also be altered as new asteroids are captured by this gravitational trap.

Already the planetoids seem to be rather free with their associations. We shall see that these vermin of the skies, like lice, seem to infect most of the planets.

Many times in this book astronomers have been described as making lists of stars, sunspots, galaxies, and other phenomena, in an effort to discern some order in nature. Naturally, someone started to list planetoids according to one property and another. About the only planetoid properties readily measurable are those connected with their orbits. When the American astronomer Daniel Kirkwood arranged the planetoids according to their orbital periods in 1866, he found surprising gaps in his chart at 4.0, 4.8, and 5.9 years. Somehow, the asteroid belt was swept clean of asteroids with these periods. The culprit was not hard to find; it was Jupiter again. The so-called *Kirkwood gaps* occur at simple fractions 1/3, 2/5, and 1/2 of the orbital period of Jupiter. A little computation showed these particular orbits were "resonant;" that is, planetoids with these periods would regularly catch up with Jupiter in their motion around the sun and receive a gravitational tug as they passed by. These tugs occurred at regular intervals, just like the pushes a child gets on a playground swing, and eventually the planetoids were catapulted out of their resonant orbits. Strangely enough, dark Kirkwood gaps also occur between the bright rings of Saturn, where the debris in the rings is swept out by the large, close satellites of Saturn.

Usually, periodic forces tend to pile things up as often as they sweep things clean (sand ripples) and, sure enough, Jupiter's influence has also swept many planetoids into groups with periods that are fractions of Jupiter's period. One of these groups is the Trojan group with a period precisely equal to that of Jupiter.

Where did the planetoids originate? Even though Jupiter sometimes reshuffles the panetoid population between Mars and Jupiter, astronomers have hoped that they could run their orbital equations backward (as it were) and reconstruct the history of the asteroid belt. If all gravitational influences ("perturbations") are included, all planetoid orbits might be traced back to their point of origin— possibly to that postulated planetary breakup. Simon Newcomb, an American astronomer with some fascinating prejudices, suggested this kind of analysis in 1860, but had no time to pursue the idea. He did, however, have time to write many popular books on astronomy and prove most emphatically that heavier-than-air machines would never amount to much.

Newcomb's idea was taken up by Kiyotsugu Hirayama, the director of the Tokyo Observatory. Most astronomers, however, were computationally lazy and doubted that the planetoids could be mathematically "tracked" back to their point(s) of origin. In several billion years, a lot of things could have obscured the trail, especially with heavy-handed Jupiter prowling the outskirts of the asteroid belt. So it happened that everyone was surprised when Hirayama found five "families" of planetoids that seemed to have been born of five different explosions rather than the single cataclysm postulated by Olbers. The Flora family, for example, with 57 members, circled the sun at 2.2 A.U. The other families had fewer members, but were just as closely related. Things looked even blacker for the planetary explosion hypothesis when other astronomers followed Hirayama's trail and located 29 points of origin. What could cause 29 separate (and very small) planetoids to explode? Perhaps, like the Trojan asteroids, these Hirayama families were the result of marriage instead of common descent; that is, gravitational forces might have caused some agglutination over the millennia.

Before looking further into the problem of planetoid ancestry, consider planetoid dispersion or the contagiousness of the planetoid plague. Planetoids are everywhere in the solar system, at least out to the orbit of Saturn. It may be that there are one or more asteroid belts beyond Saturn that we cannot detect because of distance and the small size of typical planetoids. The question is: How many planets are now infected by alien planetoids? The disease takes on two forms: 1) Direct collision with a planet; and 2) Gravitational capture in the form of satellites. The earth, its moon, and Mars are definitely pockmarked with craters that may be the result of the first form of the planetoid plague. No one would be surprised to find Venus and Mercury so afflicted. The larger planets may not have solid surfaces that bequeath such records to us. Solar system theory is at such a rudimentary stage of development that no one can now distinguish between small *natural* satellites and small *captured* satellites. Most astronomers would agree that our moon and the largest moons of the major planets are natural. But the small moons of Mars, Jupiter and Saturn may well be captured planetoids. No one can now say for certain. Some of these small satellites are at high inclinations to the planet's equatorial plane and seem likely to be infiltrators from the asteroid belt. Even Pluto drifting at the edge of the solar system may be a stray planetoid or possibly a moon "lost" from Uranus. It is pretty obvious nowadays that astronomers cannot vouch for the pedigrees of many small chunks of rock that are now wandering around the solar system or temporarily at home with some planet.

The Olbers planetary breakup hypothesis was dealt severe blows by the historical analyses of Hirayama and others. If there had been a single huge family of closely associated asteroids, a titanic explosion would have been the logical explanation for the asteroid belt. Dozens of separate explosions strained credibility so far that Olbers' hypothesis was peremptorily rejected by most scientists. The idea still lives on, despite the lack of support from the computations. Its extraordinary vitality results from the paucity of reasonable alternatives. Besides, the far-flung orbits of the planetoids still look as if they were explosion-born, and intuition sometimes conquers calculations.

The only other hypothesis that has come close to explaining the formation of the asteroid belt was the formerly discredited Nebular Hypothesis of Pierre Laplace and Immanuel Kant. In this theory that was so popular during the period when new planetoid discoveries had not jaded the astronomers' appetites, the planets were thought to have condensed from rings of material left behind in the equatorial plane of the sun during its early contraction phase. The asteroid belt was planet stuff that had failed to jell, possibly because of the gravitational influence of nearby Jupiter. Modern variations of the Nebular Hypothesis by astronomers such as Carl von Weizsacker and Gerard Kuiper have eliminated many of the original objections to primitive forms of the theory, and the Nebular Hypothesis is again gaining support.

It may be, of course, that a number of planetoids the size of the Big Four were first formed in the Mars-Jupiter gap according to some versions of the Nebular Hypothesis and then disintegrated by collisions or gravitational disruption. Fragmentation by collision certainly persists today in the asteroid belt. The asteroid belt occupies that transition zone between the inner, terrestrial planets and the outer, radically different, major planets. It could be that the planet-making process faltered momentarily and, in a moment of indecision, left behind a few million parts that wouldn't go together.

Just as the Nebular Hypothesis has been historically in and out of favor, so do we find astronomers vacillating with respect to the empirical law suggested by Titius and then promulgated by Bode. There's no question that most of today's astronomers consider it to be only a historical footnote to grace the pages of their textbooks. Bode's Law fell into the cellar of scientific esteem when it failed to predict correctly the orbits of Neptune and Pluto. In completing the last two entries of the table presented earlier in this chapter, the trouble becomes obvious.

	n	PLANET DISTANCES FROM SUN IN A.U.	
		BODE'S LAW	OBSERVED
Neptune	7	38.8	30.1
Pluto	8	77.2	39.5

Bode's Law was certainly useful in the early days of astronomy and it seems worth while to see what, if anything, went wrong at the limits of the solar system. Scientists rarely become concerned if ordinary physical laws break down when they are pressed to the limits, but Bode's Law is not an ordinary physical law because it has no known physical basis—it seems all too fortuitous.

Three possible ways to save Bode's Law come to mind: (1) Assumption that the orbits of the outermost planets have changed considerably during the lifetime of the solar system and that Bode's Law can be applied accurately only to that part of the solar system still unperturbed in its primitive (?) state; that is, Mercury through Uranus. (2) There may be interlopers masquerading as planets beyond Uranus. Pluto in particular may be a lost moon of Neptune or some displaced planetoid. (3) There may be asteroid belts or small planets beyond Uranus that have not been discovered yet. Finally, Bode's Law correctly predicted the orbit of Pluto with $n = 7$, implying (to those so inclined) that Neptune was not one of the original planets.

Such speculation is intriguing, but no amount of guessing will satisfy those who demand that Bode's Law be derived from primary physical principles; i.e., Newton's laws and some model describing the formation of the solar system. Regardless of the current disdain for the "empirical" law of Titius and Bode, some enterprising scientist may someday find that his theory of the solar system leads directly to Bode's Law.

Surely, these vermin of the heavens, the planetoids, have given more trouble than they are worth. Yet, they do have their champions. The late Dandridge Cole, an American astronautical engineer, did the most to publicize their utility in space exploration. The planetoids, according to Cole, offer many opportunities to the human race contemplating the exploration and, in the distant future, colonization of the solar system. Cole and Donald Cox have written a prophetic book entitled: *Islands in Space*. The allusion to planetoids as islands in the vastness of interplanetary space is especially apt in view of what Cole and Cox propose. According to them:

Planetoids may be used as natural "spaceships" in voyaging from one part of the solar system to another. Cole terms them "stepping stones."

Man can colonize the planetoids, possibly by hollowing out the planetoid and creating an artificial human-sustaining environment within it. (See p. 206.)

Planetoids may be excellent sources of metal and other raw materials the earth now consumes at a rapid clip. Cole has even proposed "capturing" a planetoid and maneuvering it into orbit around the earth through the use of rocket motors.

More succinctly, Cole views the planetoids as "micro-earths" that may be easier to adapt to human wants than the much larger and presumably more intractable planets. Someone must have visions such as Cole's if the human race is to see beyond the terrestrial problems of the moment. Visions are contagious; at the beginning of one of the chapters of *Islands in Space* is a quotation from President Lyndon B. Johnson, who certainly had his hands full of terrestrial problems when he stated:

"Someday, we will be able to bring an asteroid containing billions of dollars worth of critically needed metals close to earth to provide a vast source of mineral wealth for our factories."

That is something to look forward to in the distant future.

READING LIST

COLE, D. M., and COX, D. W. *Islands in Space*, Chilton Books, Philadelphia, 1964.

LEY, W. *Watchers of the Skies*, The Viking Press, New York, 1963.

MOORE, P. *The Planets*, W. W. Norton & Company, New York, 1962.

WATSON, FLETCHER G. *Between the Planets*, Harvard University Press, Cambridge, 1956.

10

THOSE LIGHTS
ON THE MOON

The moon is a dead world where nothing ever happens. So went an old dictum. For three generations minds were frozen in a mold that excluded bright lights in lunar craters, clouds of smoke and gas, and startling ruby-red patches that sometimes kindle over hundreds of square miles on this "dead" sister planet of ours. The moon is like the desert to a fast-traveling motorist—apparently prostrate and lifeless under the burning sun. Stop the car, though, and search the desert with an open mind, and a hundred species of flowers and animals may be seen. Not that such life breaks the vaunted monotony of the moon, although the possibility of lunar life cannot be completely discounted. Rather, we should not permit superficial appearances and narrow-minded textbooks to channel our thinking.

Lights have been seen on the moon ever since the first telescope gathered in the solar rays reflected from this slightly football-shaped orb a quarter million miles away.* William Herschel called attention to them in the eighteenth century; there have been scores of additional records since. For centuries lunar lights and glowing red

---

* In the Jan. 27, 1967, issue of *Science*, Barbara Middlehurst and Patrick Moore reported on their analysis of nearly 400 transient lunar events that have occurred in the last five centuries.

patches suffered the fate of sunspots on a "perfect" sun—they *couldn't* exist on a "dead" moon and therefore they were ignored. But time and truth pull off many sets of blinders; and the quickening moon is now a "hot" subject in astronomy. Lights on the moon and other peculiar changes are important to the theme of this book because: (1) They have revived the old conflict between the meteoric and volcanic lunar crater hypotheses; and (2) Some of the visual changes seem tied to the solar cycle, much like the spectral nuances on Mars and Jupiter.

This chapter is risky to write. By the time this book is published more Surveyor space probes will have landed on the lunar surface and the moon will have several artificial satellites of its own. The data radioed back from the moon's surface will probably give us a better physical picture of the moon than the past centuries of telescopic observation.

The panorama seen by a tv camera or astronaut on the lunar surface is rich in close-up detail but quite poor in overall scope. The surface of the moon curves so sharply that most of the scenery will always be just over the horizon. A man standing in the center of a large crater would see only a rather featureless plain, for the crater walls would be hidden below the horizon. The point of this short lesson in selenography is that the ephemeral and widely scattered "lights" on the moon are best detected by telescopic patrols on the earth, but knowledge of their ultimate nature will depend upon close-up work by a human or automated geologist. Astronomers on earth can guide men and machines to such localized targets of opportunity when they appear.

Such targets of opportunity were often described by early astronomers. William Herschel, the great German-English astronomer, who ground the best telescope lenses of his period and who also acquired a reputation as an organist and music teacher, is usually credited with calling astronomers' attention to these rather rare lunar displays. The night of April 18, 1787, while studying the area around the crater Aristarchus, Herschel saw spots glowing like "slowly burning charcoal thinly covered with ashes." Compare this description with that of John Greenacre, who saw a similar sight near Aristarchus on October 30, 1963, through the Lowell Observatory telescope. Greenacre felt that he was "looking into a large, polished gem ruby but could not see through it." These bright lunar "flares" last only for minutes, a half hour at the most. The descriptions of Herschel and Greenacre, so alike in quality though nearly two hundred years apart in time, typify two distinct eras in astronomical thinking. Herschel and his fellow astronomers of the eighteenth century conceived of the moon as an active, changing place and perhaps an abode of life. Herschel believed his lights were caused by volcanic eruptions. Greenacre and most contemporary astronomers do not hold out much hope for finding life on the moon, but find the lunar surface brimming with subtleties Herschel had never dreamed of. In between Greenacre and Herschel lie many decades when the "dead moon" dictum prevailed.

Red glows and light flashes are not the only kinds of observations that make the moon an exciting globe to watch. A few craters seem to have disappeared, others are new, and there are dark "bands" that seem to come and go around some craters.

One of Herschel's contemporaries, Johann Schroter, was a fervent believer in a changing moon. As chief magistrate of Lillienthal (the same town where von Zach and his planetoid "celestial police" met in 1800), Schroter evidently had ample time and money to indulge his hobby of astronomy. Schroter helped systematize lunar map drawing and kept alive the idea that the moon was not completely passive. Using one of Herschel's fine telescopes, he made hundreds of detailed maps of various sections of the lunar surface in patient, systematic German fashion. Schroter wanted to capture surface detail and then check later to see what changes had occurred, for he was certain the moon was not static. The project reminds one of the systematic sunspot drawings made by another German amateur astronomer, Heinrich Schwabe. Schroter's lunar maps proved him no artist, but they were accurate and honest. Everyone used his maps, but no one believed his claims that he saw changes in the lunar geology. Napoleon's armies brought Schroter's hobby to an end when they razed his observatory in 1813 and carried away his brass instruments, thinking they were gold.

Schroter's idea of "draw-and-check-later" eventually paid off. In 1865 the German astronomer Julius Schmidt reported that the crater Linné (named after the naturalist Linnaeus) in the flat plain called Mare Serenitatis had practically disappeared. In maps drawn as late as 1843, Linné was shown as a deep, prominent crater, eight miles in diameter. To Schmidt it was (and it still is) only a small pit on a swelling surrounded by a whitish deposit. Something had happened; but what?

Astronomers like action and many could not resist checking out the Linné report and then hunting for a few changes on their own. Soon, one of the craters near the border of Mare Crisium which Schroter had employed as a major reference point was found to have disappeared completely. A few other craters showed obvious changes. No one has been able to explain these alterations—*if* they actually occurred. It is surprising that the dogma of the changeless moon germinated and grew in the face of all the reported changes.

Before it was suppressed by dogma, volcanism flourished as the logical explanation of lunar activity. Volcanoes on earth spread fire, clouds, ash deposits, and red-hot lava flows over large regions. Conceivably volcanoes could even blow apart under the powerful forces welling up from the earth's hot interior. There was no reason why the moon should not be subject to the same natural forces.

Immanuel Kant, who was a "natural philosopher" of great breadth, advanced the lunar volcano hypothesis as early as 1785, anticipating Herschel in this respect. (Kant also promulgated the famous "nebular hypothesis" before Laplace.) For ninety years, lunar volcanism seemed a matter of only passing interest. Perhaps volcanoes did spew forth fire and lava on occasion; the idea perturbed no one, it was more important to find new planets and planetoids.

The silence was broken by two English amateurs, James Nasmyth and James Carpenter, who vigorously advanced volcanism in their 1874 book *The Moon: Considered as a Planet, a World, and a Satellite*. Nasmyth and Carpenter recognized that lunar craters were hardly even distant cousins to earthly volcanoes if appearances meant anything. The majority of terrestrial volcanoes are of the Vesuvius type, conical but with small cup-shaped depressions or vents at the top. Lunar craters, in contrast, are usually broad, shallow depressions circled by low rims. Often a small central peak at the precise center relieves the featureless surface within the circular (sometimes polygonal) rim.

The Nasmyth-Carpenter lunar volcano model was something like a Fourth of July fire fountain. They postulated a vent leading to a reservoir of magma (molten rock) within the moon. Through the vent issued a vertical stream of ashes and debris that arched out in all directions falling on the lunar surface with geometric precision in a circular rim. As Patrick Moore points out in *A Survey of the Moon,* it is hard to believe that a massive yet sharply defined circular wall one hundred miles in diameter could have been formed by such an imprecise gun. The real contribution of Nasmyth and Carpenter was the presentation of a well-defined model that scientists could either defend or tear apart and offer substitute models for. The fire-fountain hypothesis started people thinking about the crater problem again.

Another easily refuted crater theory had been proffered in 1665 by Robert Hooke, the ill-tempered critic of Newton. Hooke suggested that vast gas bubbles rose to the lunar surface when it was still molten. Upon bursting, the bubbles left a circular rim just as they do in porridge or the mud pots of Yellowstone. But no physicist can countenance a hot bubble one hundred miles in diameter in molten rock; it would collapse under pressure.

Of the many modern variations of the lunar volcano hypothesis, the most reasonable is based upon the forces that create terrestrial calderas. According to this theory, upwelling lava creates a dome-shaped mountain; part of this mountain then falls back into the cavity left behind by the ejected lava. A nearly circular rim remains. Lava then covers the central debris with a smooth surface. Two features of terrestrial calderas are found in the larger lunar craters: (1) A general depression of the crater floors below the level of the surrounding landscape, and (2) a hexagonal cast to the circular rim, most likely formed as the lava pressure forces the surface rock to break along regular fracture lines in the early stages of caldera formation. Calderas might have been formed wherever weaknesses occurred in the lunar crust. Since many lunar craters are strung in chains, lines of overlapping calderas could form along long linear fractures in the lunar crust. Scientists who favor the meteorite-impact hypothesis craftily adopt the convincing caldera model by claiming that calderas form where the crust has already been cracked and weakened by a direct hit from some celestial heavy artillery.

Early in this century, the volcano hypothesis was prematurely supplanted by the meteorite impact hypothesis. It has been revived recently and will appear again in this chapter after the rise of the dead moon dictum and the evolution of the impact theory are described.

The moon-is-dead viewpoint diametrically opposed the outlook of Herschel and Schroter, neither of whom would have been surprised to see prosperous cities of moon people through their telescopes. The idea of a dead moon was advanced by Wilhelm Beer, a German banker whose hobby was astronomy, and his friend Johann Madler. Together, these two men studied the moon care-

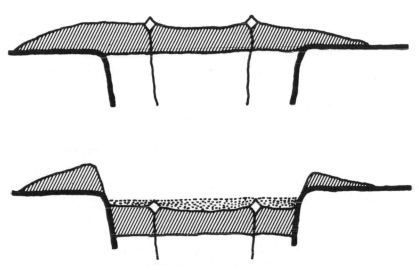

Terrestrial calderas of subsidence are formed when volcanoes slide back into the cavities created by the expulsion of lava and volcanic debris. The final crater, which may be partially filled with lava, looks remarkably like the typical lunar crater.

fully for almost ten years. They drew a detailed map that became the basis for much later astronomy of the moon. A book with the title *Der Mond* followed the map in 1838. The map and book were masterpieces of care and accuracy and promptly became authoritative references on the lunar surface. Beer and Madler had seen no lunar activity at all during their decade of observation and said so most emphatically in *Der Mond*. The book's strength as an authoritative reference infected the world of astronomy with the book's weakest conclusion. For more than a generation, astronomers turned their telescopes to other points in the heavens, for a dead, well-mapped moon could bring no discoveries, no thrills of exploring the unknown, and no fame to the observer.

Simon Newcomb popularized the dead-moon dogma in several of his books for the layman. Only one quote is needed: "The moon is a world without weather on which nothing ever happens." Lunar astronomy might have languished forever if Julius Schmidt had not found in 1865 that the crater Linné had been nearly erased from the lunar surface by a force unknown. Happily, the moon "died" for only a generation. The more astronomers study it today, the livelier it seems.

Even before Beer and Madler formally interred the moon, a new hypothesis explaining the lunar craters had been put forward by Franz von Gruithuisen, still another German astronomer. He suggested in 1828 that the lunar surface had been pockmarked early in its history by volleys of meteorites raining down from outer space. Gruithuisen was not the first to propose an impact theory. It was enigmatic Robert Hooke again who, in a feat of precognition, had postulated impact craters over one hundred years earlier. He even went so far as to drop bullets in a mixture of pipe clay and water to make craters that were remarkably moonlike. Hooke was decades before his time because no one thought it possible that stones could fall from the sky, particularly stones big enough to gouge out the immense craters seen on the moon. (Incidentally, Hooke also boiled a mixture of powdered alabaster and water to test his bubble theory of crater formation. The craters were the same shape as those created by the falling bullets.) Gruithuisen could at least point to meteorites (now scientifically acceptable) to substantiate his views. Unfortunately, he also had a vivid imagination that made his fellow astronomers look askance at his impact theory. He described a "lunar city" twenty-three miles on a side, with "dark gigantic ramparts." Although Gruithuisen lived in an age when lunar life seemed quite likely, a huge city was hard to accept. Our best telescopes today show only low, rather unorganized ridges at the site of Gruithuisen's city, just as Schroter drew the picture a century and a half ago. The meteorite impact hypothesis did not prosper when Gruithuisen proposed it.

Next to espouse the impact idea was an English astronomer, Richard A. Proctor. Although Proctor later had doubts about the impact hypothesis, he was a well-known popularizer of science who was able to impress the idea, while he held it, on many minds.

Still another impact advocate appeared, from a most unlikely quarter. Grove K. Gilbert was Chief Geologist of the U.S. National Survey. The year was 1892, recorded as "The Disaster," when half the personnel of the National Survey were laid off. Gilbert was supposedly in Washington lobbying for funds to enable the Survey to carry on with its mission. Actually, he was at the Naval Observatory watching the moon.

Gilbert wrote a friend at this period: "I am a little daft on the subject of the moon, being troubled by a new idea as to its craters, and I have haunted the Observatory for three evenings in which I have netted but one hour of observation. Clouds and congressmen are about equally obstructive." Congress had its say about Gilbert, too. One member said: "So useless has the Survey become that one of its most distinguished members has no better way to employ his time than to sit up all night gaping at the moon." The Survey lost part of its funds but science gained a paper which was presented in 1893 before the Washington Philosophical Society.

Gilbert's thesis was that the earth was surrounded by a ring of tiny moonlets after the fashion of Saturn's rings. As the orbits of these moonlets varied due to perturbations by the moon and earth, they crashed into the lunar surface, creating the craters. Gilbert reasoned that the orbital moonlets were necessary so that they would crash *vertically* into the moon and blast out the *round* craters observed through the telescope. He did not know that impact craters are approximately round regardless of the angle of impact. After substituting meteoroids for moonlets in Gilbert's proposal, the impact thesis sounded quite reasonable. Gilbert gave the theory a push that was to carry it to dominance.

Gilbert's case for meteorite impact was strengthened considerably when Alfred Wegener, the famous German geologist, carried out laboratory experiments that simulated lunar impacts by dropping powdered plaster onto a smooth layer of powdered cement. Wegener's fame came from his "continental drift" hypothesis. His reputation plus his experiment's faithful reproduction of miniature lunar craters converted many astronomers to the impact theory. Wegener's book, *The Origin of the Lunar Crater*, appeared in 1921.

Nothing could be simpler than the impact concept. An errant meteorite, traveling at tens of thousands of miles per hour, slams into the moon's rocky surface. The kinetic energy of the projectile is converted into heat and shock waves. Several things could happen next: 1) Lunar material could be simply blasted out to form the crater, like the crater from an artillery shell; 2) The heat could cause widespread melting of the lunar rock, which then would resolidify to form a smooth crater floor; 3) The force of the impact could weaken the lunar crust to the point where lava from the interior wells up to partially fill the crater.

In other words, there is enough *flexibility* in the impact process to to explain many features of lunar craters. Scaled-down terrestrial impact experiments confirm that meteoroid impact could blast out craters the size and shape of those observed on the moon.

At first, some scientists resisted conversion to the impact theory, pointing to the fact that the earth, due to its proximity to the moon, should have come under the same barrage of meteorites. And where were the craters on earth? Geologists, all strong proponents of the impact hypothesis, quickly retorted that the bombardment occurred so long ago that terrestrial erosion had wiped out nearly all traces of the earth's share of craters.

It was not until about 1906 that the astronomical community learned that a gigantic impact crater existed in the wilds of Arizona. Most scientists were incredulous, but Meteor Crater, a mile wide, is a fact—as many transcontinental air travelers can testify. Indians and gold prospectors had known about Meteor Crater long before 1906, but its existence was somehow not communicated to the astronomers. Grove Gilbert arrived at Meteor Crater in 1891, two years before his Washington paper. Although the existence of a large impact crater on the earth would have made Gilbert's paper much more believable, he concluded that Meteor Crater was the result of a "steam explosion." He considered it just a coincidence that meteoric iron was found in the vicinity. Rare it is when an avid supporter of a hypothesis overlooks such a substantial piece of supporting evidence.

The discovery of Meteor Crater was soon followed by discoveries of other impact craters the world over. Some are quite fresh (only a few million years old) and obviously the results of impact; others are heavily eroded and best seen from the air. There is no doubt in anyone's mind that *some* lunar craters are also meteorite-produced. Here, the argument turns to numbers. Impact-hypothesis supporters claim the earth is peppered with craters, enough to support their position. The proponents of lunar volcanism say just as emphatically that not nearly enough bona fide terrestrial impact craters have been uncovered to make them believe that the earth and moon experienced the same aerial bombing; therefore, many lunar craters, probably most of them, must be volcanic in origin. Nevertheless, the mere existence of terrestrial impact craters was sufficient to make many doubtful astronomers shift to the side of the impact hypothesis.

Gilbert's paper and Wegener's book helped sustain the often boisterous debate over the impact and volcano hypotheses that has continued on and off during this century. In 1949 the most formidable weapon on the side of the impact forces rolled into position. It was the publication of *The Face of the Moon* by the American astronomer Ralph B. Baldwin. The book carefully details in most convincing fashion the case for meteorite impact as the cause of *most* lunar craters. Strange how a book or paper, even if it presents only one side of a story, can be so influential. *Der Mond* had solidified scientists' thinking behind the dead moon viewpoint.

The Face of the Moon was so persuasive that scientists of all disciplines flocked to the side of the impact hypothesis. Harold C. Urey, an American Nobel Prize winner, stated the majority position in 1956: ". . . It is characteristic of science that different objective observers studying the same evidence come to the same conclusions, and that the overwhelming majority of such observers agree substantially. When this occurs, we regard the conclusions of such scientists as true. For this purpose . . . I am concluding that the volcanic hypothesis is false and the collision one is true . . ." Urey was quite correct; most scientists discounted volcanism in 1956. But scientific truth is a relative thing dependent upon consensus; a minority still protested.

Let us set aside the near consensus that prevailed in 1956 and lay the pros and cons out for inspection. To begin, two peculiar but general aspects of the controversy must be mentioned. It is rather ironic that astronomers generally side with the volcanic theory—a *geological* theory—while the geologists have historically supported the meteorite-impact position—an *astronomical* theory. The second point of interest is that *both* theories are correct; that is, craters on the moon are undoubtedly created by both processes. It is a matter of degree; not an either-or decision that has to be made.

Favoring the impact hypothesis are these observations:

Terrestrial experiments and theory conclusively show that the craters *like* those seen on the moon *could* be caused by meteorite impacts.

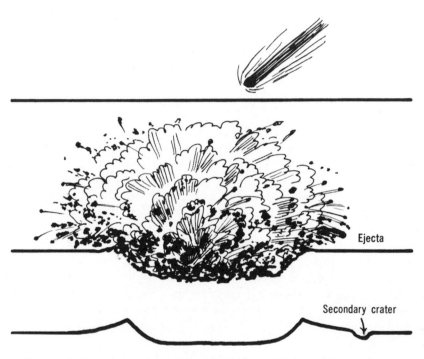

Ejecta

Secondary crater

Collision of a high velocity meteorite with the lunar surface could cause an explosion that blasts out a hole many times the diameter of the meteorite. The resulting crater, as confirmed in terrestrial impact experiments, would look very similar to those on the moon. Ejecta could form many secondary craters.

Similar but smaller meteor craters have been discovered on earth.

The quantity of lunar debris found surrounding a crater is usually roughly equal to the volume of the hole (Schroter's Rule), implying that lava upwelling did not take place.

The number of *small* craters observed on the moon seems consistent with the number of meteors now entering the earth's atmosphere when the rate of influx is multiplied by the four-billion-year age of the moon.

Lunar craters *seem* random, at least on a local basis. Note that the volcano proponents are equally positive that the lunar craters are not randomly distributed.

The light-colored rays of debris that surround many craters can be explained as ejecta arising from meteorite impact.

Many small craters, some only a few feet across, are much more easily explained as due to direct impacts of meteorites or the chunks hurled out of a nearby crater by the initial explosion.

Crater walls are usually devoid of signs of the lava flows one would expect if volcanism were rampant.

On the other side of the issue, those who favor volcanism can produce an equally impressive list of pros:

Lunar craters often form chains. Wherever two craters overlap, the larger is always interrupted by the smaller. Terrestrial volcanoes are found in similar chains.

Fifty or more lunar craters are perched on the tops of Vesuvius-like mountains in a close parallel to classical terrestrial volcanoes.

A few lunar craters are filled almost to the brim with what appears to be lava. (A meteorite impact *could* have released the lava.)

Assuming the moon has the same inventory of radioactive elements as chrondrites (rocky meteorites), there would have been ample heat evolved from radioactive decay to create the lunar craters through volcanism. Some studies of lunar radioactivity suggest that the amount of radioactive heat released may be increasing.

Terrestrial craters bear a striking resemblance to many lunar craters.

Many lunar craters occur in chains (*not* at random) that could hardly have been caused by undisciplined meteorite salvos. (Even many meteor enthusiasts concede that crater chains are probably volcanic in origin.)

Lunar craters are not at all random even when the obvious chains are eliminated.

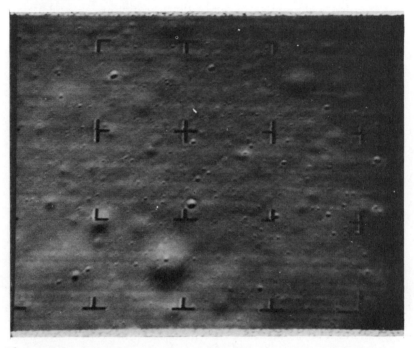

Photograph of the lunar surface taken by a Ranger space probe just before impact. Note the large number of craters; some are just a few feet wide. (NASA.)

Wherever craters overlap, the larger crater is almost always broken into by the smaller. Meteorite believers have to assume that all the large meteorites fell early in the process to explain this observation, a very unlikely situation. In terrestrial volcanoes the larger eruption nearly always occurs first.

The many lights and red spots seen over the centuries *may* indicate continued volcanic action on the moon. (Alternative interpretations will be presented shortly.)

Some of the lunar rocks televised by the Surveyor spacecraft show the rounded contours and porosity typical of ejecta from volcanoes, although it is also possible that the rocks may have been melted by the heat of meteorite impact.

In summary, good cases can be made for both the meteoric and volcanic theories. Consensus has swayed to one side or the other as new facts have developed down the years. No one doubts that lunar craters have been created by both mechanisms. Only manned landings and extensive geological surveys will tell us which and how many craters owe their births to one type of cataclysm or the other.

A composite of several photographs taken by the Surveyor space probe showing a large lunar rock in the vicinity of the spacecraft. This rock shows the rounded contours and porosity of volcanic ejecta.

Turning once again to the subject of lunar changes, scientists are no longer artificially restricted by the dead-moon dogma. It is now the other way around. Many astronomers are certain that changes occur and have been occurring all the time; furthermore, once again they are actively looking for changes, just as Schroter did 150 years ago, but with incomparably better instruments. Present research falls naturally into these categories: bright lights, luminescence, enhanced surface brightness, clouds and obscurations, structural changes, and thermal hot spots. Almost all of these "modern" (meaning: "finally recognized") phenomena bear on the crater controversy in one way or another. As the subsequent discussion will indicate, the tendency today is to explain many such apparitions with still a third force: solar stimulation of physical and chemical processes.

Bright lunar lights, seen frequently since the first telescopes were trained on the moon, are commonly dismissed as reflections of sunlight from lunar structures or possibly light generated by the impact of a large meteorite. Starlike lights have often been seen in the crater Aristarchus and seem best explained as solar reflections from structures that reveal their presence only when sunlight hits them just so. A good analogy would be the flashes seen by aircraft passengers from house and car windows on the ground. The observation of the English astronomer F. H. Thornton is typical. On April 15, 1948, while studying the crater Plato, Thornton was startled by a brilliant orange flash a half mile or so from the crater wall. The flash was similar to that of the explosion of an anti-aircraft shell. Such flashes are too brief to indicate the presence of volcanic activity, although they might well be due to meteorite impacts. Naturally, science-fiction fans have alternate explanations of a more artificial nature: i.e., "signals."

The setting for the next manifestation of lunar activity is the large crater Alphonsus, seventy miles across, and famed for dark patches that change shape. Alphonsus has been no stranger to lights and other "unusual" occurrences, but an observation by Dinsmore Alter on October 26, 1956, began a modern surge of enthusiasm for lunar research. Alter was photographing Alphonsus at Mount Wilson Observatory with red and blue filters. He noticed that the crater was invisible on some photographs taken with the blue filter, although the surrounding terrain was clearly defined. With the red filter, the crater was visible. Alter suggested that this "obstruction" might be due to the presence of gas in the crater that absorbed the blue light. Other astronomers had noted many similar obscurations in the past, but it was Alter's discovery that led to the next scene of this drama, which has already become a scientific classic.

Stimulated by Alter, the Russian astronomer Nikolai A. Kozyrev, at the Crimean Astrophysical Observatory, began a systematic study of the interior of Alphonsus with his spectroscope. On the night of November 3, 1958, Kozyrev photographed the spectrum of a reddish patch that he attributed to fluorescent gases issuing from the crater's central peak. The reddish patch seemed to move and disappeared after a half hour. The spectrum showed the well-known bands characteristic of the molecule C_2, possibly at a temperature as high as 2000°C. The whole Alphonsus story was pooh-poohed by some; but similar activity was again noted in Alphonsus on October 29, 1959, and within the notoriously variable crater Aristarchus in 1961 and 1963. The observations and the observers making them are too reliable to be ignored. The Alter-Kozyrev sightings gave heart to the hard-pressed adherents of the volcano hypothesis of crater formation.

In October and November 1963, several important sightings, such as Greenacre's, were made from Lowell Observatory. Briefly, glowing red patches were seen by several competent Lowell observers in the neighborhood of the crater Aristarchus. One patch on the outer rim of the crater was twelve miles long and a mile and a half in breadth. Some of the patches persisted for over an hour. The observations were strikingly like those made by Herschel in 1787. A historical search revealed that almost two dozen outbreaks had been seen in the Aristarchus area since Herschel's time.

Even the "obscurations" had a respectable ancestry. In his 1954 book, *Our Moon*, H. Percy Wilkins notes several occasions when familiar details of well-known craters could not be seen. Some experienced observers ascribed these periods of poor seeing to lunar "mists." It is tempting to connect the obscurations to the red patches; the latter being a visible outbreak of volcanism and the former invisible gases released during less violent activity, say, the release of pockets of subsurface gas.

Red spots, clouds of gases; they seem convincing enough to make one jump on the volcano bandwagon, but, stimulated by observed lunar changes, a major non-volcanic interpretation has evolved within the last few years.

One significant recent observation is that the brightness of the moon changes as much as 20% during the solar cycle, being brightest at the peak of the sunspot cycle. Conceivably, whatever solar mechanism enhances lunar brightness—probably white luminescence—may also generate localized red luminescence on occasion.

Just as subtle are isolated dark patches that come and go, fade and darken on the lunar surface. A blackish patch seen clearly by all early observers of the moon on the floor of the crater Petavius has now disappeared entirely. In contrast, none of the early astronomers saw the dark radial bands that are now prominent in the crater Aristarchus. Complete appearance and disappearance of dark features is rather rare, though changes in prominence are very common. *Moving* dark patches have been reported and cannot be ignored. The American astronomer William H. Pickering claimed that spots in the crater Eratosthenes do move, covering about twenty miles in twelve days. He surmised they might be swarms of insects. This interpretation is intolerable in the light of present knowledge of the near vacuum, intense ultraviolet flux, and violent hot-cold cycle on the moon's surface. Something, however, is happening that enhances and erases dark spots. Again, the causative agent may be solar, volcanic, or something unsuspected.

Patrick Moore in his book *A Survey of the Moon* devotes a whole chapter to the many lunar formations that have changed radically over the years or winked out altogether. There are new appearances of craters, and other geological structures too. Such changes are *not at all common* and some probably should be classified as optical illusions. The moon is not dead, but its metabolism is certainly low.

The infrared detection of "hot spots" on the moon really gives us a kind of X-ray vision that sees below the surface. When the lunar surface is bathed in direct sunlight, it is very hot indeed, well over the boiling point of water. During an eclipse of the moon the earth's shadow drops temperatures rapidly to below the freezing point of water. The moon, however, does not cool uniformly. Some spots cool more slowly because they are covered with a thick layer of insulating dust. Solar heat has sunk deep into such areas and when the sun is blotted out the stored heat is conducted slowly back to the surface. Still, there are many thermal anomalies that cannot be explained by the idea of a varying dust layer. When the moon is scanned during an eclipse by an infrared detector, a tv-like picture of lunar hot spots is constructed. There are hundreds of them. Some hot spots concentrate in certain areas, such as Mare Tranquillitatis; others are associated with bright spots on the moon; still others are unrelated to any visible feature. All in all, lunar thermal anomalies or hot spots are *not* randomly distributed and are *not* correlated with any particular type of lunar surface feature. They *could* identify thermally active areas on the moon; that is, localities of past, present, or future volcanism.

With eye alone, terrestrial astronomers would see lunar volcanism as reddish flows of lava, occasional flames from large eruptions and, of course, ash deposition. Volcanism can explain a lot of the observed transient activity. Lunar history demonstrates, however, that it is easy to jump to false conclusions. The assumption of lunar volcanism may be just such an unwarranted leap. Besides, the problems of lights, luminescence, and the ephemeral dark colorations confront the astronomer no matter where he looks; they infect all the planets. The enhanced radiance of the *whole* moon at the peak of the sunspot cycle, which is hard to attribute to volcanism, might well tie in with a *non-thermal* explanation of lunar and planetary optical activity from Mercury through the major planets.

Light and bombardment by subatomic particles stimulate luminescence in many common minerals. The common mineral fluorite, for example, gets its name from the fact that it fluoresces* brightly under ultraviolet light. From this observation, it is only a short step to the hypothesis that lunar and planetary luminescence can be stimulated by solar electromagnetic radiation and the streams of particles emitted during solar storms.

How can one prove the existence of non-thermal luminescence and then distinguish it from volcanic outbreaks?

Whenever the sun is suspected of stimulating activity of some sort, the first impulse is to try to correlate solar activity with the phenomenon of interest. Positive correlation strongly implies solar

---

* *Luminescence* is a general term applied to all light emitted as a result of non-thermal energy addition. Fluorescence is that part of luminescence that ceases once the source of energy is shut off; i.e., the ultraviolet lamp in the case of fluorite.

involvement. In the case of overall lunar luminescence, the correlation is positive and obvious. The highly localized "volcanoes" of Herschel and the recently seen flares of Greenacre and other astronomers do not correlate well with solar events in all cases. The October 1963 observations of Greenacre were made just forty-eight hours after an intense flare erupted from the sun. A few other lunar flashes also seem to be related (after a time delay) to specific solar flares instead of the overall sunspot cycle. Thus, the impression rises that direct, almost instantaneous bombardment by solar photons is not the stimulant. Rather, the slower particles accelerated across interplanetary space by solar flares cause the moon to luminesce in selected areas. Such solar plasma tongues collide with the earth's magnetopause, causing magnetic storms and auroras (Chapter 6). The moon logically should receive a share of these energetic particles. The solar particles would impinge on materials on the lunar surface, activating specific minerals that then release the energy of activation as light visible to us through the telescope.

Another line of research has discovered that certain meteoric materials will luminesce under bombardment by protons with the energies found in solar plasma tongues. Unfortunately for the hypothesis, the number of such particles in the plasma tongues does not seem adequate to stimulate the bright patches seen on the moon. If the plasma could be "focused" somehow, the energy requirements would be satisfied.

The thought of focusing recalls the observed fact that flareups on the moon are sporadic and highly localized, occurring around Aristarchus and a few other notoriously active craters. Not all solar flares provoke a lunar response and sometimes lunar red spots occur on the dark areas of the moon. It seems as if a hose is spraying the moon with solar plasma. Strangely enough, such a plasma firehose exists; it is the magnetic "tail" of the earth that lashes the moon with its trapped radiation flux. Since the earth's tail always points away from the sun, it should spray the moon around the time of the full moon. The tail would help focus particles to meet the energy requirements of luminescence and would also add another element of variability to the rather haphazard displays of lunar activity. Luminescence on the moon, then, may depend first upon a flareup on the sun and second upon the earth's magnetic tail (which probably wags erratically) channeling some of these particles to potentially active areas on the moon. This chain of events is a little long to be particularly convincing, but it seems feasible. The credibility of the mechanism is supported by the observation that intense luminescence has always occurred when the moon was near full.

Granted an erratic stream of stimulating solar particles, why are some spots on the moon activated while others remain indifferent to bombardment? It may be that the moon always displays luminescence at Aristarchus and other craters when sprayed by solar plasma, but that the necessary stream of plasma is rare and irregular. By this assumption, active areas on the moon are those where the proper minerals are always on the surface and exposed directly to the plasma bombardment.

If the plasma stream is not so localized, there must be some erratic activity on the moon that exposes luminescent material. Moonquakes, volcanic action, and meteorite impacts could all stir up the lunar surface to uncover luminescent material. It may be that much of the lunar dust seen in the Surveyor photographs is naturally luminescent but the thin surface layer is so damaged by solar radiation that luminescence is impossible, unless some disturbance brings fresh material to the surface.

Lunar luminescence is a new subject for astronomy. It is in that rudimentary state where many ideas are rampant. A decade from now scientists will probably laugh at some of the mechanisms suggested above. The moon, however, unquestionably luminesces over its entire sunlit face and reddish glows over areas as large as 50,000 square miles have been reported. These displays are most easily attributed to solar-induced luminescence. The high localized, ruby-red spots seen by Herschel, Kozyrev, Greenacre, and many others may be either luminescence, volcanism or some phenomenon we do not yet recognize. Only time and the landing of astronaut-geologists will tell.

In addition to Pickering's insect swarms, there are other fanciful explanations of lunar lights and physical changes. The great French astronomer Nicolas Flammarion was also confident that he had detected changes on the moon's surface. Like Pickering, he felt that such changes could only betoken the presence of life—vegetation, in his mind. Perhaps it is unkind to this famous popularizer of science to note that he vigorously backed Lowell and his Martian canal hypothesis and later in life abandoned astronomy for psychical research. Near the top of the list of wilder hypotheses has been the repeated suggestion in science fiction that the lunar craters are actually the result of an ancient nuclear war between lunar beings and the earth or Mars or some other abode of intelligent life existing several billion years ago.

The best-known fanciful idea relating to lunar craters is the Ice Theory, which was energetically promulgated by the German H. Horbiger. According to the Ice Theory, the craters are merely lakes of frozen water. As the lakes cooled after their formation, the water vapor rising from them condensed around their margins to form the crater "rim." The Ice Theory encompassed the entire solar system, not just the moon. In *Fads and Fallacies*, Martin Gardner relates how the Ice Theory acquired millions of followers in the mystical, anti-intellectual atmosphere of Nazi Germany.

Completely unrelated to Horbiger's views are the more reasonable, modern suppositions that water and ice may still survive on the moon in sheltered spots that never receive the full light of the sun, or under thick insulating blankets of dust. If the moon was formed from the same stuff as the earth, water must have been present in abundance during its early history. Some propose that geysers, steam vents, and dust covered glaciers may still exist.

The mention of glaciers brings to mind the well-publicized suggestion of Thomas Gold (also a cosmologist, see Chapter 1) that dust on the lunar surface may be rendered fluidlike if particles acquire electrostatic charges under solar irradiation. Electrified dust particles then might "flow" down inclines and accumulate in the plains and other depressions. The fact that the Surveyor lunar probe did not founder in a quagmire of fluidized dust has made most scientists discount the dust hypothesis. Its picture also showed exposed lunar rocks in abundance rather than a landscape drowned in dust.

The moon's display of visible changes, particularly lights, red flares, luminescence, and structural alterations have brought forth theories involving three important and radically different causative agents: meteorite impact, volcanism, and sun-induced luminescence. That all three phenomena occur to some degree on the moon now seems incontrovertible. The real question concerns how much lunar activity is due to which cause. The possible origins of the lunar craters are tied intimately to the visible effects in the sense that the latter are clues about the former. Again, it is not either one cratering mechanism or another, but rather how much volcanism and how much impact cratering took place over the moon's history. The astronauts of Project Apollo are journeying to a world that is radically different from ours. They should bring back not only the answers to our questions about lunar activity but mysteries far deeper than mere "lights on the moon." From a distance of a quarter million miles, we can be sure that the moon is far from dead and that alone is sufficient to whet the appetites of scientists and astronauts alike.

READING LIST

ALTER, D. *Pictorial Guide to the Moon,* Thomas Y. Crowell Company, New York, 1963.

BALDWIN, R. B. *The Face of the Moon,* University of Chicago Press, Chicago, 1949.

————. *The Measure of the Moon,* University of Chicago Press, Chicago, 1963.

FIRSOFF, V. A. *Strange World of the Moon,* Basic Books, New York, 1959.

————. *Surface of the Moon,* Hutchinson, London, 1961.

KOPAL, Z. The Luminescence of the Moon, *Scientific American,* 212, 28, May 1965.

————, ed. *Physics and Astronomy of the Moon,* Academic Press, New York, 1962.

————. Topography of the Moon, *Space Science Reviews,* 4, 737, September 1965.

LEY, W. *Watchers of the Skies,* The Viking Press, New York, 1963.

MOORE, P. *A Survey of the Moon,* W. W. Norton & Company, New York, 1963.

11

THE SEARCH FOR
LIFE BEYOND
THE EARTH

In the fourth century B.C., the Greek philosopher Metrodorus remarked: "It seems absurd that in a large field only one stalk should grow and in an infinite space only one world exist." Most people, scientists included, still feel this way. Space *seems* boundless and life on earth is so rich and varied that a single, unique abode of life amidst this plenitude is nigh unthinkable. So goes popular thought. So go scores of books telling of the likelihood of life on Mars and the hundred billion other planetary systems that may harbor life.

But, if all these things are so, "Where is everybody?" Where are the alien spaceships landing to welcome us as members of a galactic empire? Where are friendly radio signals from across the interstellar void? Where is *one good hard fact* indicating the presence of extraterrestrial life, even the lowliest microbe?

Some shreds of evidence do favor the existence of life beyond the earth, but the facts are "soft" and subject to non-life interpretations. The hypothesis that extraterrestrial life exists wants supporting data, say, of the quality of the planetary observations that substantiate Newton's Law of Gravitation. Short of having an extraterrestrial being appear in person before the National Academy of Sciences, hard evidence of other life "out there" will be long in coming.

The question is like any other scientific question: it depends upon consensus; whenever a majority of qualified scientists believes that the evidence for extraterrestrial life is adequate, it will then be a

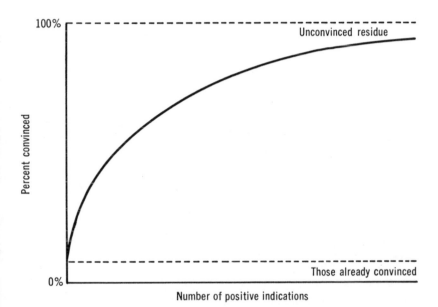

The number of scientists believing in the existence of extraterrestrial life increases with each new positive indication, but there will always be a residue who will consider the evidence insufficient or suspect.

"scientific fact." Like the obsolete phlogiston theory or the luminiferous ether, the fact of alien life once "proven" would be subject to modification and even outright refutation. Each new positive indication of extraterrestrial life—evidence of chlorophyll on Mars, for example—will convince more and more scientists. As positive facts accumulate, a majority of the scientific community will be persuaded accordingly. Unanimity, however, will never prevail because some die-hards would never change their minds short of a trip to Mars to examine the canals firsthand.

Suppose that our trips to Mars reveal only a barren, cratered wasteland, absolutely sterile. What if the "ears" of our radio telescopes hear nothing but meaningless squeak and gibber through the oncoming centuries? Most of us will feel pretty lonely, but the die-hards (of a different sort) will still be with us. "It is impossible," they will say, "to search the *entire* universe and therefore one cannot conclude that extraterrestrial life does not exist." True enough; but science and taxpayers would probably tire of such negative sport long before any manned expeditions to Jupiter and the other major planets left the launch pads. Pure speculation about life leads nowhere. Credit the human race with curiosity and energy. Enough people now believe that extraterrestrial life is possible to spur the nations of the earth to mount assaults on the moon, Mars, and Venus with instrumented probes and manned space vehicles.

No one would be particularly satisfied if a spacecraft landed on Mars and transmitted back a mere yes or no, life is or isn't here. We want to know a great deal more than the mere fact of existence or nonexistence. The first expedition to Mars (or the moon) might find one or more of the following:

Protolife, where chemical evolution has progressed to a point where molecules that are precursors to life (for example, amino acids, fatty acids, etc.) are present in detectable amounts under environmental conditions suitable for the synthesis of still more complex molecules.

Primitive life, where protolife has become reproducing, metabolizing, and mutating.

Diverse forms of animal and vegetable life, including perhaps intelligent life.

Artifacts or fossils from a once-living biosphere and possibly even culture.

Equipment belonging to nonindigenous life.

No evidence of life.

Something beyond our present knowledge; that is, *life as we do not know it*. (A good example would be obviously intelligent radio signals or messages with a discernible but unbreakable code.)

An experiment to detect extraterrestrial life would have to be extremely versatile to encompass all the possibilities mentioned in the foregoing list. While a human biologist-astronaut might be adaptable enough to reconnoiter a new planet thoroughly, life-detection instruments by themselves are very specialized, as later discussions will prove. An instrument designed to detect white rabbits on Mars might completely miss green lizards. The discovery and elucidation of extraterrestrial life is going to be much more of a challenge than the explanation of Jupiter's Great Red Spot.

The well-traveled journalistic road first summarizes the meager evidence for life beyond this earth and then concludes that gathering more such evidence must be man's major occupation in outer space. We will concentrate on the varied and contending hypotheses about extraterrestrial life and just what data are needed to resolve them, taking the reader off the crowded thruway up into the clear air of high-country logic where the real subtleties of extraterrestrial biology (exobiology) are easy to discern.

One day in the early seventies, an unmanned spacecraft will brake itself with its rockets to a soft landing on the Martian surface. Among the arms, wings, and antennas that unfold from this craft will be sensors from several life-detection experiments. What questions will these sensors ask of Mars? One category of questions will inquire into the *origin(s)* of whatever life may be discovered. A second kind of question will ask about the *nature* or *character* of this life.

The questions about *origin* will be the most difficult to ask. No single experiment could ever say which of these three hypotheses is most likely to be true:

Life originated spontaneously.

Life has existed forever and was never "created."

Life was created by supernatural powers.

Each question asks indirectly: "What is man? Is he an isolated quirk of nature, part of a universe-wide phenomenon, or the handiwork of God?" Obviously, a lot of voyages to Mars and, for that matter, to the rest of the universe will be required to gather any really significant evidence.

If a robot of man, a hundred million miles away on Mars, televises back a picture of a field of lichen-like growths, who can say how they got there? They may be an indigenous species surviving through the billions of years from the time when Mars was fecund with warm seas and a thick atmosphere. Or, the lichens may have evolved from "spores" that continually drift through all of space, the same ones that infected the earth. Or, God may have decided to create life many times in many places in various guises. Life detection, in itself, cannot help decide between the three hypotheses of origin. A yes-or-no answer is useless.

Indeed, no amount of science can ever disprove God, since, as the Creator, he could put life anywhere at any time. Science, therefore, recognizing its weakness in this respect, concentrates on the two hypotheses of spontaneous generation and infinite existence.

The hypothesis of spontaneous generation holds that life will arise without outside interference wherever and whenever conditions are right. Some highly suggestive terrestrial experiments along these lines will be described shortly.

The second idea—that of life existing forever and perpetuating itself by pervasive fertile spores through the universe—is closely related to the famous "panspermia" hypothesis. Panspermia says essentially that life has been carried from one spot in the universe to another by spores or "seeds" of life, under the influence of radiation pressure or some other motivating force. Evidence for panspermia would certainly not disprove multiple spontaneous creations of life, but it would undeniably strengthen the infinite-life hypothesis. The infinite-life hypothesis depends, naturally, upon panspermia that is infinite in both space and time.

Cosmological problems arise here. If the Big-Bang Model of the universe is correct and we live in the only universe there is, there cannot be anything like infinite panspermia, for what spores of life could survive the high temperatures of periodically coalescing ylem? "Aha," argues the panspermist, "all spores might not be drawn into the Big-Bang and some might survive to infect the cooling planets created after the Big-Bang." If other Big-Bang universes are permitted, life might survive in the cool ones to reinfect those sterilized by the Big-Bang. While infinite panspermia can be forced into the Big-Bang mold, it is philosophically right at home in the Steady-State model of the universe. Life would course through an infinite universe coexisting with matter, light, and even time itself, with no beginning and no end.

These are large thoughts for a hundred or so pounds of protoplasm on a cool pebble circling a most ordinary, middle-aged star. What an ironical turn of events if the only spark of life among all the seas of stars originated, resides, and philosophizes on earth.

But we must enlarge the panorama with science to see what does lie beyond our earth. First, the terrestrial evidence for spontaneous generation of life and panspermia.

Not so long ago, everyone *knew* that eels were created spontaneously in wet fields illuminated by the March sun. Or was it worms from horsehairs in the horse trough? It does not matter, there were

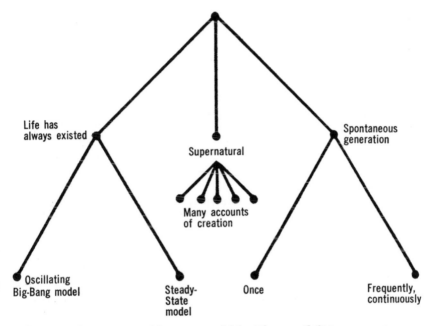

Schematic showing possible origins of life. The possibilities are not necessarily mutually exclusive. Panspermia could occur with any of the possible origins shown.

hundreds of such "superstitions," as we now label them. For a while, Pasteur decisively routed such delusions by "proving" experimentally that life always derived from life. (Apparently Pasteur himself still believed life might sometimes originate spontaneously.) Today, despite Pasteur's experiment, we try to make life in test tubes. No one has yet made life in the laboratory, but most scientists seem to think it can be done on the basis of several suggestive experiments.

In 1952, Harold C. Urey, an American Nobel Prize winner in chemistry, argued that the earth's primitive atmosphere probably consisted of hydrogen, ammonia, water vapor, and methane, and that these molecules spontaneously united to form the basic building blocks of life. Following Urey's lead, Stanley L. Miller, a student of Urey's at the University of Chicago in 1953, prepared a sterile brew of water and the suggested chemicals. An electrical discharge in the sealed container simulated the ultraviolet energy of the sun. After a few days, Miller detected a wide variety of organic molecules as well as a few amino acids in his simulated primordial soup. The simple experiment made a big impression. It must enter any discussion of the possibility of extraterrestrial life.

Miller's experiments were carried further by C. Sagan, C. Ponnamperuma, and R. Mariner in 1963. Taking some of the organic molecules spontaneously synthesized in Miller's experiment, and subjecting them to ultraviolet light, they created adenosine triphosphate (ATP), a molecule critical in energy transfer in earth organisms.

The distance from relatively simple amino acids and ATP to an organism that metabolizes, duplicates itself, and has the potential for evolving into higher forms of life is a long one. The universe, though, has had billions of years rather than a few weeks to do its cookery, and it has had many pots bubbling on an immense variety of stoves. No one can claim that spontaneous generation of life has really been proven by such simple experiments, but they are suggestive. The experiments of Miller, Sagan, et al. have greatly increased the credibility of the hypothesis of spontaneous generation of life as well as the existence of extraterrestrial life.

Solid proof of the spontaneous generation of life could come along either or both of two paths. The wide gap between the creation of life and the amino acids might one day be bridged in the laboratory. Or, if a spacecraft ranging far beyond the solar system found multitudinous life springing from a wide variety of alien environments, many would be convinced that spontaneous creation had often taken place. If the concept of panspermia were thoroughly discredited at the same time, the case for multiple spontaneous generation would be greatly strengthened.

Like spontaneous generation, panspermia has a history reaching back beyond the written record. Apparently man has always firmly believed in the universality and fecundity of life and its innate capability to transport and regenerate itself. Terrestrial experience favors this outlook, but does the theory hold across billions of light years?

Greek philosophers of the fourth century B.C. first promulgated the idea that seeds, spores, or "ethereal germs of life" were spread throughout the length and breadth of the universe. Anaxagoras and Leucippus are generally credited with the basic concept of panspermia though many refinements came later. The concept also found favor among the Romans, including St. Augustine and the early Christians. Times change, though, and Giordano Bruno, who championed panspermia in the sixteenth century (along with other heretical ideas), was burned at the stake for his trouble.

In the work of Lord Kelvin and Hermann von Helmholtz, panspermia became *lithopanspermia* in the nineteenth century. As the name implies, lithopanspermia relies upon rocks, specifically meteorites, to carry the seeds of life throughout the universe. This is a logical thought because simple forms of life, protected by rocky shells, might safely survive the deadly radiation of space and searing heat of entry into planetary atmospheres. Furthermore, a life-bearing planet does not have to explode like a snapdragon to scatter the seeds of life; the impact of a large meteorite can blast pieces of a planet's crust off into space. There is considerable evidence, for example, that a special variety of meteorite found on earth, called a *tektite,* may have been blown from the moon's surface by meteorite impact.

Radiopanspermia was conceived by the great Swedish chemist Svante Arrhenius, who also coined the word *panspermy* to describe his idea. A common physics laboratory demonstration in Arrhenius's time was that of radiation pressure. Arrhenius reasoned that out in space, far away from strong gravitational fields, radiation pressure might be sufficient to "blow" tiny spores like microscopic sailboats from place to place in the universe. Bacterial spores are extremely hardy and can survive high doses of radiation. Arrhenius believed that the rock shields of micrometeorites were unnecessary to panspermia. Radiation levels in space, however, have proven to be quite high and travel times between planetary systems are extremely long; radiopanspermia has fallen into general disfavor today.

Science-fiction writers have incorporated the idea of *artificial panspermia* in many plots. Here, some usually benevolent galactic race goes from planet to planet sowing the seeds of life. Further, there is accidental or unintentional artificial panspermia, as spacecraft carry microbes around the universe. It is possible that the Americans and Russians between them have already infected the moon and Mars with incompletely sterilized space probes. Biologists on future manned voyages may find circles of contamination spreading out around defunct spacecraft like fairy rings of mushrooms.

Actual collection of interplanetary spores and/or fertile meteorites would strongly support the panspermia hypothesis; but no such experiments are planned at the moment. If, however, in the distant future, life is found to be not only widespread throughout the universe but possessing similarities attributable to a few varieties of intersellar seeds, panspermia would again be strengthened. Of course really convincing proof of panspermia will be elusive. Proponents of spontaneous generation can always argue that any similarity of life from planet to planet derives from the fact that the basic chemical units of life are similar, just as snowflakes are forced into a hexagonal mold by the molecular forces holding ice crystals together.

One of today's burning "life" questions centers on a rare type of meteorite called a *carbonaceous chondrite*. Most meteorites picked up after falling are either "iron" or "stonelike," but the carbonaceous chondrites are black, earthy, and crumbly. After a chondrite had lain exposed for a few years in a farmer's field, an experienced meteorite hunter could walk right past it without seeing it. The first recorded fall of a carbonaceous chondrite occurred on March 15, 1806, in southern France. Surprised by rumbling and cannon-like noises in the skies, French farmers saw two black masses fall from above and smash into the ground. A number of warm, blackish fragments were collected. The Swedish chemist J. Jakob Berzelius received one of the fragments some twenty-eight years later and could scarcely believe that it was a real meteorite. Nevertheless, he analyzed it and found a rich assemblage of organic compounds much like those found in garden soil. "Does it," he asked, "possibly give an indication of the presence of organisms on extraterrestrial bodies?" If meteorites, which rain down on the earth an estimated

10,000 tons of extraterrestrial matter a day, truly carry life, panspermia, at least within the solar system, would seem a reality.

Down the years other scientists noted the chemical peculiarities of the carbonaceous chondrites, but the vigorous modern debate over their nature did not begin until March 1961. Working with fragments of the famous Orgueil meteorite that had fallen near the village of Orgueil in southern France in 1864, Bartholomew Nagy, Douglas J. Hennessy (both of Fordham), and Warren G. Meinschein (formerly of Esso Research and Engineering Company) announced that they discovered a rich lode of hydrocarbons similar to those found in living matter on the earth. Shortly afterward, microscopic studies of the Orgueil meteorite turned up not only contaminating terrestrial microorganisms but also peculiar "organized elements." Nagy and George Claus, a microbiologist from New York University, published a paper in the British journal *Nature* that described five classes of shapes that looked suspiciously lifelike. Some were spherical with protuberances; others cylindrical with finely sculptured wall surfaces. Some of the organized elements looked so much like terrestrial algae that they were given scientific names, such as *Caelestites sexangulatus* (six-sided thing from the heavens).

The experienced reader will recognize immediately that here we have all the makings of a classical controversy of science. A doubter can question the validity of the basic observations, like those astronomers who could not see the Martian canals; or one can claim that the meteorite under examination was contaminated by terrestrial organisms whilst it lay on a museum shelf for many decades; finally, a hoax can be declared. All strategems have been tried by the forces that reject the life-in-meteorites idea. As a matter of fact, one fragment from the Orgueil meteorite apparently was tampered with, biologically-speaking, many years ago. Although this revelation was welcomed by the anti-life forces, it did not rule out the many recent analyses of the many different carbonaceous chondrites that show organic content. Most argument has turned about the contamination factor. Apparently ragweed pollen and other "seeds" can slip into the meteorites and confuse the issue. Also possible is the nonbiological creation of rather complex organic compounds, like those mentioned earlier in experiments on spontaneous generation. (Even petroleum *may* be formed abiogenically.)

The controversy still rages. The flames might subside if the first astronauts on the moon found similar carbonaceous chondrites with like inventories of hydrocarbons and lifelike "organized elements." The charge of contamination might also be removed if a highly respected scientist (even better, a group of them) was to see a meteorite fall, pick it up, rush it to a laboratory while still warm, and find in its deepest recesses those same organized elements.

If life forms in the final test prove to be native to carbonaceous chondrites, where could they come from? A rather startling response is: *"The earth, of course."* Undoubtedly, meteorite impacts in the past have flung life-bearing bits of the earth's crust into space; some may have reached escape velocity and afterward circled the sun for eons until one day they returned to shock some French farmer. If this sort of explosive scattering of earth life can occur, our astronauts may find earth life everywhere they go in the solar system. On the other hand, the moon, Mars, or some asteroid may have given birth to life and later infected the earth in this localized form of lithopanspermia. Quite obvious by now is the difficulty in disentangling the seed source from the gardens that sprang from it; it is like trying to find the original tree that seeded a huge forest of Douglas firs.

A more frivolous, but still not completely ridiculous, topping to the panspermia story is the suggestion that carbonaceous meteorites are an intentional legacy from some former denizen or visitor of the solar system that wished to leave some indestructible, information-packed sign of its past presence. Perhaps science had better look at those organized elements more carefully to see their real message.

Having failed to make much headway (in the scientific sense) in identifying the wellspring(s) of life, we hope for better luck in unraveling the nature of extraterrestrial life. By "nature," is meant: What is extraterrestrial life like, especially in contrast to earth life, and still more specifically in contrast to human life?

The ladder of principal alternatives shown here starts with the basic query: Is there extraterrestrial life or isn't there? Assuming that there is life beyond the earth and sidestepping the just-muffed question of ultimate origin, the next two possibilities are that it is either *life as we know it* or *life as we do not know it*. These are classical categories but they are also rather fuzzily defined. A

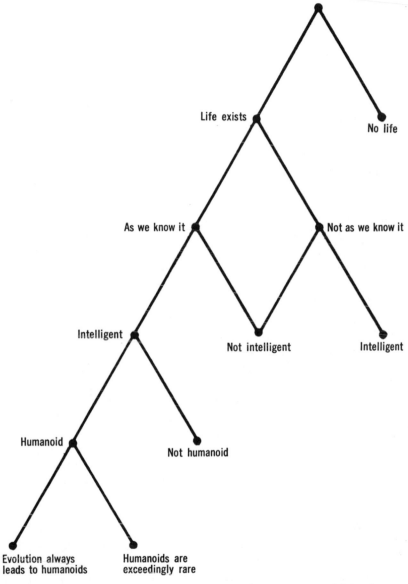

Schematic showing possible characteristics of extraterrestrial life. Again, the possibilities are not mutually exclusive.

very human-appearing extraterrestrial being (a humanoid) might (stretching credulity a bit) employ silicon rather than carbon in his chemical makeup. Much as we might enjoy playing chess and drinking beer with this humanoid, we would have to put him in the bin marked: Life as we do not know it. On the other hand, some bug-eyed monster (BEM) might scare us out of our wits and yet still be life as we do know it. Earth life is so varied that it is hard to imagine *really different* kinds of life. At the moment, no rationale for separating the two classes exists. It may be that the division cannot be made and all life is *life as we do know it.* This would, of course, be evidence for universal panspermia.

Regardless of whether we are cousins once or one hundred times removed from an example of extraterrestrial life, the next distinction is one of intelligence. What is really meant is: Is this creature smarter than I am? If it is, presumably it will be asking the questions and the problem is easily solved. The usual mazes and intelligence-testing devices of the terrestrial laboratory could be applied if man were obviously superior. Levity aside, intelligence is another hard-to-define item—hardly anyone attaches much significance to IQ scores anymore. An intelligence scale that is difficult to apply to earthlings would probably be impossible on an alien planet.

The next classical question asks whether the alien creature just captured is a humanoid; that is, blessed with an abundance of human external characteristics. This distinction should be fairly easy to make because it depends upon appearance only. The humanoid seems to be found mostly in science fiction, where empathy with alien characters is proportional to their degree of humanness. In the real universe, intelligent alien life, if it exists at all, would most likely have followed an entirely different evolutionary course. Most exobiologists are convinced that other humanoids are infinitely unlikely.

Or are they? This question brings up the rear in a series of philosophical speculations. Farfetched though it may be, there may be a unity of life in the universe that we cannot see because we know of only one sample—earth life. There *may* be one or just a very few channels down which evolution flows. Atoms, to illustrate, go together in only certain ways to form molecules. Large molecules, like those common in life processes, are built of certain building blocks that must fit together *just so*. It is true that the immense number of variations possible in the structures of genes and chromosomes have produced an awe-inspiring panorama of living and extinct life forms; but the "trees of life" so prevalent in biology textbooks have strong central trunks with heavy limbs leading off the trunks. Perhaps we should not be surprised if we find an alien creature with bilateral symmetry, red blood, and a big brain. It verges on mysticism to insist that life once started *always* leads to humanity; but, though life is complex, it may not be infinitely so, and one of the thruways of evolution may lead straight to (and past) man.

The ancient Greeks firmly believed in the universality of life and tried to support this intuition by formulating the *subhypotheses* of spontaneous generation and panspermia. Life is everywhere on earth; on every continent, in the Antarctic ice and the boiling springs of Yellowstone, at the top of Everest and in the Marianas Deep, in all the nooks and crannies of this globe. The Greeks, and our forefathers, too, had ample reason to extrapolate their observations to the moon and planets which, as far as they could tell, were much like the earth. The ubiquity of life on a celestial scale seemed doomed, however, when science looked at the planets more closely and found them without agreeable atmospheres or either too hot or too cold. But this negative view of just a few decades ago is now being dispelled as the planets and, most importantly, life itself, are studied more closely. The rather fragile evidence presented below has made science "cautiously optimistic" (to use current technicalese) about the chances of finding extraterrestrial life.

The only *direct, in-hand* evidence we have of extraterrestrial life consists of the carbonaceous chondrites, which is evidence so questionable that no trial lawyer would give it a passing thought. Three other classes of evidence exist:

Probability computations of the numbers of habitable planets in the universe and the likelihood that they harbor life.

Signs of life on the planets (Mars in particular) and experiments showing that terrestrial life *might* survive on other planets.

Signals from other civilizations.

In the near future (the early seventies), a fourth category, that of direct life-detection experiments on the surfaces of other planets, will be added as spacecraft land on Mars. A remote chance exists of finding life or the residue of life on the moon before 1970.

If you wished to compute the probability of having identical twins, you could take past experience as a guide, dividing the number of twins born per year by the number of total births. The same technique might be used in computing the likelihood of finding life on Mars, *if* we had previously explored a lot of other planets like Mars. Because we haven't, *probability calculations based on experience* are out of the question in exobiology.

Nevertheless, a scientist must be able to predict to win his daily bread. When a foundation of experience is not available, say, in the form of Newton's laws, he makes "educated guesses," which are sometimes good, sometimes bad. To estimate the number of abodes of life in the universe, the scientist must first know the number of star systems with warm, womblike planets. Stellar temperatures are hardly conducive to life and neither are those of perpetually frozen spheres, such as Pluto. The elements in the calculation are: the number of stable star systems that have planets, the number of such planets that have been in existence long enough to develop life (spontaneously or by seeding), and the probability that life will develop given these inviting conditions.

The astronomer Harlow Shapley has suggested that perhaps one star in a thousand has a planetary system. We know of one for sure, the sun. In addition, Barnard's star and several other stars seem to have large, dark bodies circling them. Shapley's educated guess at least had some observational foundation. From here on, though, the guesses are more intuitive than educated. Suppose that only one star system out of every thousand with planets has its planets spotted at a distance that provides the right temperatures. The product of these two probabilities leaves only one star system in a million with planets of the right temperature. Two other requirements, each of which requires a thousand-fold reduction in the probability of life, are the need for an atmosphere and the stipulation that oxygen must be present. Customarily, one planet with the right conditions per trillion stars (10^{12}) is assumed—a conservative guess. It is then assumed that life will *always* appear on such suitable planets.

The whole probability process reminds one of efforts not so many centuries ago to compute the number of angels dancing on the head of a pin. Knowing the size of the pin and the average dimensions of an angel, some pretty good estimates could be made—assuming the angels were going to dance in the first place. In other words, the calculation of fertile planets may be orderly and rational for the most part, but it is not supported by observations of the real world.

What science really does in such a probability calculation is express in numbers a *belief* that the universe is so big and so festooned with seemingly infinite galaxies that it is unthinkable that only one planet, ours, should be chosen to evolve life. The probability argument is equivalent to Metrodorus'—that "only one stalk in a large field" is a ridiculous notion. To complete the probability calculation, one cosmological model estimates that there are 10^{21} stars in the universe. Multiplying this by 10^{-12}, it appears that 10^9, or one billion stars *probably* have planets supporting life. In truth, of course, there may be none at all save the earth or there may be an infinite number, if you care to believe in an infinite universe.

Moving from educated guesses to observational facts, the planet Mars sends to us several signs of life via the telescope and spectroscope. The telescope shows us Martian polar caps that recede in the Martian spring. A "wave of darkening" accompanies this "melting" of the polar cap and proceeds toward the equator. Qualitatively and subjectively, this sequence conjures up an image of polar caps melting under the weak, but warmer, spring sun, releasing water as a liquid or ground-hugging vapor that gives life to dormant vegetation as it sweeps southward (or northward, in the southern hemisphere). Unhappily for the hypotheses invoking Martian life, "abiogenic" or non-life mechanisms can cause a darkening wave. To illustrate, Mars has seasonal wind patterns that in the spring could progressively strip fine dust off elevated regions, which then become dark either because the particles left are larger or because they are naturally dark-colored. The dust hypothesis is just as reasonable as a declaration of Martian life. The choice of the life hypothesis seems highly subjective.

The dust hypothesis—not the only abiogenic scheme—also accounts nicely for the observation that dark areas covered during a dust storm soon "regenerate" themselves as if plants shook off or worked themselves up through the thin covering layer. The dust promoters claim that the thin layer would quickly disappear as prevailing seasonal wind patterns returned after the dust storm.

Now, the life hypothesis would be greatly strengthened if the spectroscope conclusively showed the polar caps to be water ice and the dark areas verdant with plantlike spectra. Over the last few decades various interpretations of polar cap spectra have indicated the presence of frozen water, frozen carbon dioxide (dry ice), and N_2H_4. The anti-life forces always gleefully promulgate news of the existence of polar-cap compounds other than water. In truth, the whole matter is unsettled, despite the "conclusive" proofs claimed by the newspapers and popular books. Obtaining and interpreting the absorption spectra of a small white spot on a tiny, rather cold planet tens of millions of miles away is tricky business. All three compounds mentioned may be present, plus others still undetected.

Most exciting of all spectrographic explorations of Mars—to the life enthusiasts, at least—were those by the American astronomer William M. Sinton in 1959 and 1961. In the infrared region of the spectrum, he discovered that the dark areas of Mars (supposedly covered with vegetation) showed three absorption regions at 3.45, 3.58, and 3.69 microns.* Many hydrocarbon molecules absorb light at 3.45 microns and absorption in the 3.69-micron region is typical of acetaldehyde. The presence of Martian organic matter was a reasonable inference from these facts. For about five years, the "Sinton bands" were ballyhooed as the best proof of life on Mars. The cautious warned that many inorganic chemicals show similar absorption regions in the infrared, but for many the case for life was now proven. Then, heavy water molecules (HDO) in the earth's atmosphere were indicated as the culprits; they absorbed some of the infrared photons in the 3-4-micron region. The spectroscope pointed at Mars does not say *where* the absorbing molecules are along the line of sight, just that something somewhere is soaking up photons. The Sinton bands are now highly suspect.

Since life-detection experiments cannot yet be undertaken on the Martian surface, the next best thing is to recreate the Martian surface in the terrestrial laboratory and see if life will prosper. "Life" here must mean terrestrial life. The presumption is that if terrestrial life can survive under simulated Martian conditions, then some

_____
* A micron is one millionth of a meter.

kind of life can exist on Mars—providing that life is there to begin with.

A sealed container simulating the Martian equatorial environment would provide diurnal temperature extremes of roughly $-94°F$ to $+70°F$. Atmospheric pressure would be perhaps one fortieth that of earth (25 mm Hg) and nitrogen would make up well over 90% of the total; 2–3% of carbon dioxide and less than 0.1% of oxygen would be added to the nitrogen. A sandy soil with just a trace of moisture would make the floor of the experimental chamber. For complete simulation, an artificial sun would shine on the specimens of terrestrial life with slightly less than half the sun's intensity on the earth. One major and possibly critical difference in Martian sunlight would be the presence of a strong ultraviolet component that is filtered out by ozone in the earth's atmosphere. Germicidal lamps employ ultraviolet light, so the lack of ozone high in the Martian atmosphere might deter the development of life on that planet.

Since the 1950s, many groups have built Mars simulators. The famous "Mars Jars" at the Air Force School of Aerospace Medicine typify the early work. Microorganisms in pulverized sandstone from the Painted Desert survived and even prospered during lengthy sojourns in the Mars Jars. More recent experiments of a similar nature demonstrate that a few terrestrial plants, such as cucumbers, could sprout, grow, but not flower in a Martian environment. Even insects can survive a few weeks. Lichens are particularly hardy and continue to live despite an ultraviolet flux several thousand times that which they experience on earth.

Martian environment experiments demonstrate, first, the hardiness of terrestrial life forms, and second, that Mars is not uncompromisingly inimical to life. The most such experiments can do is reduce the level of surprise if life is eventually found on Mars. No one has yet had the courage or financial backing to determine which, if any, terrestrial life forms can survive the much more severe environments of the moon and Venus.

The evidence for extraterrestrial life collected thus far is inconclusive. By 1980, however, manned landings and scientific automata aimed at other solar system planets should answer this question one way or the other insofar as the solar system is concerned. It may be a century before the earth can send unmanned probes toward those nearby star systems adorned with suitable small planets. Another century may pass before the probes arrive at their destination and we receive a few weak telemetry signals across those light years of space that make our solar-system planets look so cozy and gregarious. For those who cannot wait for technology to give birth to the faster-than-light rockets and the matter transmitters of science fiction, an alternate avenue is open: if we cannot go to other civilizations, maybe they will come to us or at the very least talk to us by radio. Already they may be trying to contact us. Or, they may already have done so and the message have gone unheeded.

If Lowell's ideas about networks of Martian canals can be discussed rationally and unemotionally, so can the unusual radio signals picked up by early terrestrial experimenters. Nikola Tesla was an unappreciated and rather eccentric Croatian-American electrical engineer. Not only did Tesla win out over Edison on the issue of A.C. versus D.C. power, but he also claimed to have received the first interplanetary radio communication. During his 1899 experiments with wireless transmission of power in Colorado, Tesla's equipment registered periodic signals "with a clear suggestion of number and order." Tesla could not identify them with any known natural or artificial sources of electromagnetic disturbances. He reported: "Although I could not decipher their meaning, it was impossible for me to think of them as having been entirely accidental . . . a purpose was behind these signals . . . they are the results of an attempt by some human beings, not of our world, to speak to us by signals. . . . I am absolutely certain that they are not caused by anything terrestrial." Though he lived until 1943, Tesla refused to reveal the full details of these peculiar signals.

In September 1921, while aboard his yacht *Elettra*, Guglielmo Marconi picked up what he termed an "interplanetary communication." The signals, which were "high in the meter band," were regular and apparently coded. The only letter in Morse that Marconi made out was a "V." He believed the signals had originated somewhere out in space. By some strange coincidence, Marconi himself had repeatedly transmitted the code letter "V" in his early wireless experiments in 1899.

Other early short-wave experimenters, notably Dr. David Todd, professor of astronomy and a scientist with many controversial suggestions, noted other strangely regular signals, some recurring periodically. Those were days when the radio spectrum was not bursting at the seams with AM, FM and tv programs, but there were enough diathermy machines and other electric equipment around to make any such experiments suspect. Even more peculiar were the "echoes" of shortwave transmissions reported by B. van der Pol and C. Størmer in 1927 and 1928. Several observers in Europe had picked up the experimental signals transmitted by Størmer and van der Pol but only after delays of several seconds. It was as if something was reflecting or playing back the signals. The time delays involved were so large that distances at least as great as that from the earth to the moon were necessary for pure reflection. The puzzle of these echoes has never been solved.

Reading down the history of anomalous radio reception, it is striking to note the number of "echoes," that is, receipts of terrestrial signals transmitted earlier, delayed sometimes by seconds or, in two well-known cases, twenty-two years. Some courageous speculators have suggested that a nearby alien civilization might sow unmanned radio repeaters near those planets that seemed to be developing life. The most obvious way for the alien machine to attract attention from earth would be by parroting the signals it received. Carrying the "model" a step further, this alien civilization, located eleven light years or so away, was tipped off about the emergence of terrestrial technology via its instrumented earth-watching alarm device and has probably had us under close scrutiny for several decades. Thus runs the tale of anomalous radio signals. Like the Martian waterways, a fascinating superstructure has been constructed upon a weak, skimpy foundation of facts, facts found by one or a few observers and unlikely to be repeated for scientists in general.

Except for Todd's experiment during the 1924 opposition of Mars, receipt of extraterrestrial radio signals—if such they were—was purely accidental until April 8, 1960, when Project Ozma was inaugurated. Frank Drake, leader of Project Ozma, named his program after the Princess of Oz, that imaginary land populated by exotic beings. The plan behind Ozma was the systematic "listening" for extraterrestrial signals from two nearby stars suspected of having planets, Tau Ceti and Epsilon Eridani. Listening would be done around the frequency of 1420 megacycles, the prominent "tone" emitted by interstellar hydrogen. The "ear" was the 85-foot radio astronomy telescope at the National Radio Astronomy Observatory at Green Bank, West Virginia.

Project Ozma was begun with a minimum of fanfare, because ridicule was expected from many scientific quarters for wasting valuable telescope time on such will-o'-the-wisps as voices from alien civilizations on distant stars. The caution was well-advised, for when the news of Ozma hit the scientific community it predictably split it into two contentious factions: the scoffers and the rooters.

Save for some initial excitement ostensibly caused by classified airborne radar countermeasure experiments, Project Ozma heard nothing during 150 hours of listening attributable to conversation-minded extraterrestrials. The Project obtained a null result; null results can be useful to science as exemplified by the Michelson-Morley experiment, but the Ozma scoffers have made a very weak "no" concerning alien life into a most emphatic "no" to further research along these lines. Project Ozma has never been resumed. No one can doubt, though, that radio listening will continue—approved or unapproved, publicly or surreptitiously, for who can resist for long a ringing telephone or possible signals from other civilizations?

The evidence for extraterrestrial life is easy to summarize: To the tough-minded scientist, there are only the vaguest of hints, so weak that they may be conveniently forgotten; to those with a little mysticism in their makeup the door leading to the most important discoveries in mankind's history is still ajar and still beckoning.

In our present state of ignorance about the origin and distribution of life throughout the universe, what actions can we undertake to satisfy hungry curiosity about our place and destiny in the universe? Terrestrial biology experiments will continue to search out the wellspring(s) of earthly life, but the prospects for finding extra-terrestrial life, particularly intelligent life, are so low that many scientists disparage further efforts along these lines. The chances of finding alien life may be slight, but *they are zero if we do not try at all*. Naturally, scientists involved in the space effort believe the search for life should be instituted at once, terrestrial astronomers and biologists maintain that available funds are better spent on ground-based experiments. No one but the government can finance a space probe to Mars. In the United States space program, the decision has been made at least to look for extraterrestrial life on

Mars using unmanned space vehicles that will brake themselves to soft landings on the Martian surface. There is no formal search program for the moon because of the near-universal agreement that the moon is sterile.

Scientists and engineers have expended a great deal of ingenuity in the design of special instruments to detect Martian life from small, unmanned spacecraft. If a tv camera mounted on the spacecraft transmitted a Martian panorama showing obvious vegetation, or perhaps even fossils of a biosphere that died billions of years ago, science would have the most satisfying kind of proof that spontaneous generation occurred elsewhere in the solar system or that some form of panspermia took place. Although we shall ultimately see close-up pictures of the Martian surface, similar to the Surveyor moon photos, scientists must plan to detect those forms of life that are most likely to be denizens of Mars, and these are invisible to the tv camera. Microorganisms have been selected as the targets of the life hunters. On earth, microorganisms, such as bacteria, inhabit every bit of sand in every conceivable environment. They have populated land, sea, and air almost since life began. Furthermore, they are abundant, hardy, easy to catch, and ideal for radio-controlled hunting from distances of a hundred million miles.

To catch a Martian microorganism, all a machine has to do is gather in a small sample of dust, dirt, or rock with a small vacuum cleaner or sticky string. If Martian microorganisms are anywhere near as ubiquitous as those on earth, a sample of Martian life would be easy to acquire.

The thing to do with a dirt sample is to look at it—with a microscope, of course. The pneumatic system that retrieves the dirt sample from the Martian surface can blow particles onto a "sticky" focal plane in a remotely operated microscope. Any microorganisms would then be observed directly. Possibly even skeletons or fossils of long-dead species could be discerned with such an instrument. The nonlife interpretations and potential terrestrial contamination factors that afflict other life-detection instruments would be largely eliminated.

Several purely physical tests for life are possible:

The sample can be radiated with light to see if bioluminescence occurs.

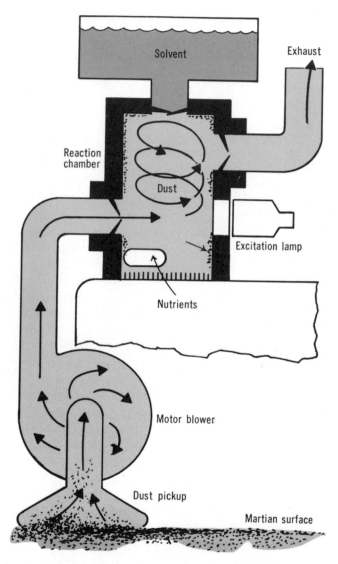

Sketch of a typical life-detection instrument, showing sample-collection scheme and reaction chamber where growth, metabolism, or some other property is measured. (After W. Vishniac.)

The sample can be dissolved and light passed through the solution to see if the plane of polarization is rotated. Life-associated molecules (such as sugars) generally rotate the plane of polarization in a specific way.

Life-associated molecules may also be identified by infrared and ultraviolet spectroscopy.

A mass spectrometer can also identify the heavy molecules in a sample by electromagnetically separating them according to their masses.

The four physical tests just mentioned do not detect life per se, but rather the chemicals associated with life. The presence of amino acids on Mars, for example, would strongly infer but not prove the existence of life. The spontaneous generation experiments of Miller et al. have shown that heavy, life-associated molecules can be created by non-living mechanisms.

Chemical means for identifying Martian molecules are also available to the exobiologist. Chromatographs are common in the chemistry laboratory and can be nicely modified for remote operation on Mars. They are much simpler than any test-tube "wet chemistry" experiment that might be applied to molecule identification.

More convincing than the identification of an amino acid would be the observation of some typical life process, such as metabolism. (At least, metabolism is typical of terrestrial life.) One life detector in this class has been dubbed "Gulliver" after Swift's character who searched for unusual life in far-off lands. Gulliver employs radioactive tracers to detect the evolution of carbon dioxide from a sample that is automatically fed with food that earthly microorganisms seem to appreciate. No CO_2 evolution, of course, would signify that a sterile sample had been brought into the instrument. Another detector of Martian life is the "Wolf Trap," named after its inventor Wolf Vishniac rather than any potential prey. In the Wolf Trap, Martian dust is vacuumed up from the surface and fed nutrients. Usually, products of metabolism from a well-fed collection of microorganisms will cause the pH of the solution under test to change. A pH meter is therefore incorporated into the Wolf Trap. If the microorganisms captured by the Wolf Trap prosper under its loving care, they will reproduce themselves (another life-indicating property) and cause the solution to become cloudy (turbid). The Wolf Trap shines a beam of light through the culture solution and measures its intensity as a function of time. A decrease in intensity would signal a cloudy solution and possibly the reproduction of Martian organisms.

But would they be Martian organisms? Just about all life-detection instruments suffer from the charge of "terrestrial contamination." It is virtually impossible to completely sterilize a spacecraft and its instruments with chemicals or high temperatures. Earthly "bugs" hang onto life with such tenacity that we can never be absolutely sure that some terrestrial microorganism hasn't crept somehow from the rocket fuel (hydrocarbon fuels are crawling with bugs) into the life-detection instrument.

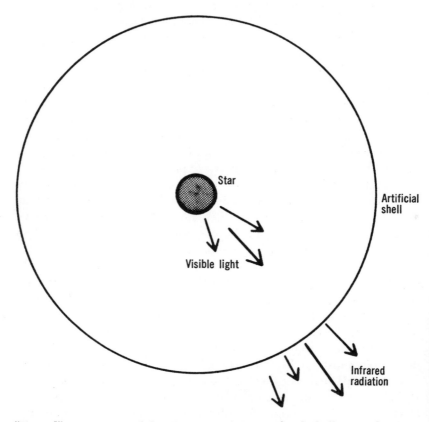

"Tamed" sun proposed by Dyson uses an artificial shell around a star to intercept all radiation, utilize its energy, and reradiate waste heat from outside shell. The shell might be tens of millions of miles in diameter.

Beyond sending rockets to the nearby solar system planets and again turning the radio ears of Project Ozma toward nearby stars, what other concrete steps can be taken in the search for extraterrestrial life? A rather startling suggestion has been made by Freeman J. Dyson, an American physicist, namely: Look for infrared stars. Dyson argues that a civilization in another stellar system would quite likely be far ahead of us technically. (We have had a technical civilization on earth for only a few hundred years out of the several billion years since the beginning of life.) Such a civilization would probably have consumed all of its natural inheritance of fossil and nuclear fuels and turned to another source of energy: its sun. Dyson thinks it possible—even probable—that a very advanced civilization could and would build a shell of energy converters around its sun to catch and utilize all of its prodigious power output. We may do the same thing within the next thousand years. With a tame star for power, a civilization could then begin real plans for interstellar travel. A star shrouded by an artificial opaque shell would not be a point of visible light to us, but rather a source of infrared radiation, peaking say at a temperature of 100°F, as the waste heat from the energy converters is dissipated into cold space. No natural object in the heavens would look quite like a star tamed by an aggressive technical civilization, and finding such an object would be tantamount to finding life.

As long as credulity has been stretched this far, a second scheme for finding extraterrestrial life can be proposed. Instead of "wasting" untold millions of man years in searching likely stellar systems by rocket, we terrestrials might decide to dispatch a steady stream of unmanned messengers—call them automata—along the plane of the Milky Way, where most stars are concentrated. As these messengers course through interstellar space they may occasionally stop briefly on suitable asteroids to replenish their fuel and propellant, and even to reprdouce themselves in order to maintain a constant density of messengers as the waves recede from the earth. Impossible? Not for the technology of tomorrow. Already we know we can synthesize fuels and propellants from materials found around a star system, and self-reproducing machines have been under study for decades.

Are such grand accomplishments futile and undeserving of the effort, just as the Great Pyramid, Grand Coulee Dam, and manned landing on the moon were called futile by those who could not

Dandridge Cole's concept of a hollowed-out asteroid supplied with an earth-like environment for purposes of colonization.

keep the pace? Not really, because out there in the stars there may be other civilizations, other systems of philosophy, other avenues to God. Knowledge and appreciation of the universe delimited by the few hints and clues scattered through the solar system must forever be sorry, puny things. Science and technology, despite their limitations and blind spots, are our only known conveyances to these new lands that may hold the answers to our deepest questions.

READING LIST

ALLEN, T. *The Quest, A Report on Extraterrestrial Life*, Chilton Books, Philadelphia, 1965.

BOEHM, G. A. W. Are We being Hailed from Interstellar Space?, *Fortune*, 63, 144, March 1961.

CAMERON, A. G. W. *Interstellar Communication*, W. A. Benjamin, Inc., New York, 1963.

CORLISS, W. R. *Space Probes and Planetary Exploration*, D. Van Nostrand Company, Princeton, 1965.

DRAKE, F. D. *Intelligent Life in Space*, The Macmillan Company, New York, 1962.

HOROWITZ, N. H. The Search for Extraterrestrial Life, *Science*, 151, 789, Feb. 18, 1966.

HUANG, S. Life Outside the Solar System, *Scientific American*, 202, 55, April 1960.

JACKSON, F., and MOORE, P. *Life in the Universe*, W. W. Norton & Company, New York, 1962.

OPARIN, A., and FESENKOV, V. *Life in the Universe*, Twayne Publishers, New York, 1961.

OVENDEN, M. W. *Life in the Universe, A Scientific Discussion*, Anchor Books, Garden City, N.Y., 1962.

SHKLOVSKII, I. S., and SAGAN, C. *Intelligent Life in the Universe*, Holden-Day, New York, 1966.

SIMPSON, G. G. "The Nonprevalence of Humanoids," *Science*, 143, 769, Feb. 21, 1964.

SULLIVAN, W. *We Are Not Alone*, McGraw-Hill Book Company, New York, 1964.

INDEX

Abetti, G., 87
absolute magnitude, 73–74, 75, 76
absorption phenomena in the atmosphere, 21
Achilles, 151
albedo, 149
Allen, T., 206
Almagest, 72
Alpha Centauri, 59
Alter, Dinsmore, 172–173, 179
Anaxagoras, 187
Andromache, 149
Andromeda, 10
  Great Nebula in, 3
apparent magnitude, 73, 74
Aristotle, 12, 52 fn., 89
Arrhenius, Svante, 187
Asimov, I., 142
asteroids, 106, 129, 143–157, 206
  Trojan, 152, 154
Astraea, 148
astrology, 103
Astronomical Units, defined, 144
astronomy, radio, 27–28, 32, 117, 119
astrophysics, 86
Atkinson, Robert, 77–78
Augustine, St., 187

auroras, 88, 91, 92, 96, 97, 100, 101, 102, 104, 105, 176
automata, 205

Baade, Walter, 10, 13, 28 fn.
Baldwin, Ralph B., 167, 179
Balmer series, 30, 31
Barnard, Edward, 132
Barnard's star, 194
Barnett, L., 70
Baum, W. A., 111
Becquerel, Henri, 44, 55, 69
Beer, Wilhelm, 163, 164
Bergmann, P. G., 70
Berlin Observatory, 145
Berzelius, J. Jakob, 188
Bessel, Friedrich Wilhelm, 72, 108
Bethe, Hans, 78, 79
Big-Bang Theory, 10, 11–17, 19, 20, 23, 48, 49, 51, 184
Big Dipper, 71
Bigg, E. K., 121
blue giant stars, 8
blue stars, 26–27, 28, 71
Bode, Johann, 145, 146, 147, 155, 156
Bode's Law, 144, 145, 146, 147, 150, 155, 156